GRADE

4

adjective

subject

pronoun

FLASH
FORWARD

Language Arts

predicate   cause   effect

Written by **Shannon Keeley**

Illustrations by **John Haslam**

© 2009 by Flash Kids

All rights reserved. No part of this publication may be reproduced,
stored in a retrieval system, or transmitted, in any form or by any means,
electronic, mechanical, photocopying, recording, or otherwise,
without prior written permission from the publisher.

Cover illustration by John Haslam
Cover design by Loira Walsh
Interior design by Gladys Lai
Production by Design Lab NYC, Inc.
Edited by Hilda Diaz

Flash Kids
A Division of Barnes & Noble
122 Fifth Ave
New York, NY 10011

ISBN: 978-1-4114-2732-7

Please submit all inquiries to FlashKids@bn.com

Printed and bound in the United States

1 3 5 7 9 10 8 6 4 2

Communication, both written and oral, is vital to success in school.

Language Arts encompasses these essential skills. Through almost 100 pages of entertaining language exercises for fourth-graders, this workbook covers important topics such as reading comprehension, phonics, grammar, vocabulary, writing, and speaking.

Flash Forward Language Arts features mazes, puzzles, and activities designed to help your student develop grammar, spelling, and writing skills. Your student will learn to compare and contrast, identify word origin, analyze cause and effect, and understand figurative language. This workbook also includes plenty of creative writing exercises and practice in numerous test-taking formats, including multiple-choice and open-ended questions.

The activities in this workbook are designed for your student to handle alone, but your assistance and interaction can greatly enhance the learning experience. As you work through the activities together, challenge your student to stretch his or her skills. Remember, however, that some concepts here will be new and require patience to master. Offer your student plenty of praise and support. After the completion of each page, you can check the answers at the back of the workbook. Use incorrect answers as an opportunity to review and rework.

In addition to working together on the pages of this book, you can encourage language skills through everyday activities. Here are some simple, age-appropriate ways to incorporate writing and oral skills into daily life. Ask your student to:

- Compare and contrast two characters from a favorite book, television show, or movie
- Give step-by-step directions for playing a game, creating a craft, or cooking a simple recipe
- Write a poem using figurative language
- Compose a persuasive essay on a topic of personal importance
- Use context clues to identify unknown words in everyday reading

These and dozens of other activities are excellent ways to help your student develop essential communications skills. Remember, language is everywhere!

Sounding Off

Sometimes the same letters can make different sounds.

For example:

l<u>o</u>ve (ə)

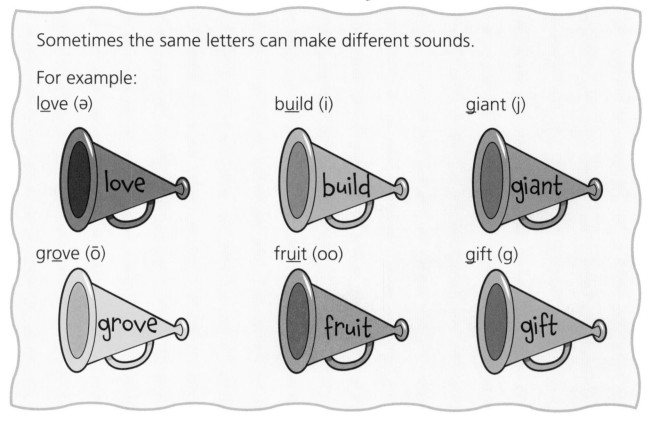

b<u>ui</u>ld (i)

gi<u>a</u>nt (j)

gr<u>o</u>ve (ō)

fr<u>ui</u>t (oo)

<u>g</u>ift (g)

Read each phrase. Circle the word that fits the description.

1. same vowel sound as *cough* call rough goat

2. rhymes with *honey* funny phone monkey

3. vowel sound made in the word *break* long e long a short e

4. *y* makes the same sound as in *by* gym happy shy

5. rhymes with *shower* grower pour hour

6. vowel sound made in *guide* long u short i long i

7. rhymes with *burn* learn born run

8. same beginning sound as *circle* sugar scene cast

The Maine Idea

The **main idea** tells what the passage is mostly about.

Read each passage. Circle the sentence that **best** explains the main idea of the passage.

1. Maine is crawling with lobsters! In fact, about 90% of all lobsters caught in the U.S. are from the coast of Maine. The fishermen must measure every lobster they catch. If it's not big enough, they must throw the lobster back into the sea. These rules help lobsters to live for a long time.

   a. Lobsters live for many years off the coast of Maine.
   b. There are too many lobsters in Maine because they live for a long time.
   c. Maine has a lot of lobsters because the fishermen follow rules to help the lobsters live longer.
   d. Fishermen in Maine must throw the small lobsters back into the sea.

2. Many lighthouses along the coast of Maine have been standing for more than 100 years. Some lighthouses have been turned into museums. Visitors learn about what life was like for the families who lived there many years ago.

   a. Visiting a lighthouse is a great way to learn about Maine's history.
   b. Lighthouses teach us about what life is like today in Maine.
   c. Some lighthouses in Maine are more than 100 years old.
   d. Maine has many museums where people can take tours.

   Write a sentence to explain the main idea of each paragraph below.

3. Do you have a bag of blueberries in your freezer? They probably were grown in Maine. The state produces about 75 million pounds of blueberries every year! Most of these blueberries are frozen or canned, then shipped all over the country and the world.

   _____

Caught in a Plot

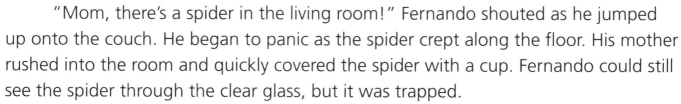

> **Plot** is what happens in a story. It tells what the problem is in the story and how the problem is solved.

"Mom, there's a spider in the living room!" Fernando shouted as he jumped up onto the couch. He began to panic as the spider crept along the floor. His mother rushed into the room and quickly covered the spider with a cup. Fernando could still see the spider through the clear glass, but it was trapped.

"Let's find out what kind of spider it is!" his mother said. She brought the laptop into the living room and she and Fernando looked up spiders on the Internet. Soon, they learned that the spider they had trapped was not harmful.

"I still don't want it hanging around inside the house," Fernando said. He carefully slid the cup along the floor to the front door. "You're free, my friend," he said as he lifted up the cup and watched the spider scamper into the front yard.

1. Which sentence **best** explains the plot of the story?

   a. Fernando is afraid of spiders and does not want any spiders inside the house.

   b. The story takes place in the living room of Fernando's house.

   c. A spider gets caught inside a cup and Fernando and his mother must find a way to get it out.

   d. After learning more about the spider trapped in a cup, Fernando decides to set it free.

2. Think of a story to go along with the picture below. Explain what would happen in the beginning, middle, and end of your story. Then write one sentence that explains the plot of your story.

   Beginning: _____

   Middle: _____

   End: _____

   Plot: _____

Sentence Styles

A **declarative** sentence makes a statement.
For example: *I'm getting myself a stylish new outfit.*

An **interrogative** sentence asks a question.
For example: *Is this coat too big for me?*

An **imperative** sentence gives a command.
For example: *Bring me this coat in a smaller size.*

An **exclamatory** sentence expresses strong emotion.
For example: *Wow—I've never looked so great!*

An **incomplete sentence** is missing something. It does not have both a subject and a predicate.
For example: *The coat with the big red buttons.*

Read each sentence. Add the correct ending punctuation mark.
Then write whether the sentence is *declarative*, *interrogative*, *imperative*, or *exclamatory*. If the sentence is incomplete, write *incomplete*.

1. Try on the smallest jeans first ☐ _____

2. What are you wearing to the party ☐ _____

3. Before you buy the shoes with the polka dots ☐ _____

4. I can't believe she spilled punch on her skirt ☐ _____

5. Shopping for a new pair of winter boots ☐ _____

6. This T-shirt is comfortable ☐ _____

Look at the picture. Write one of each type of sentence about it.

7. Declarative: _____

8. Interrogative: _____

9. Imperative: _____

10. Exclamatory: _____

Count & Connect

A **syllable** is a part of a word. Each syllable makes one vowel sound.

A-mer-i-can cheese

let-tuce

ham-bur-ger

Read each word. Count the number of syllables.
Match the words that have the same number of syllables. Write the letter on the line.

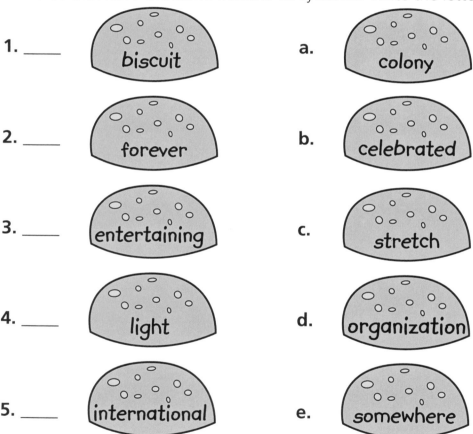

1. ____ biscuit

2. ____ forever

3. ____ entertaining

4. ____ light

5. ____ international

a. colony

b. celebrated

c. stretch

d. organization

e. somewhere

Divide each word below into syllables.

6. ketchup _____

7. watermelon _____

8. tomato _____

9. avocado _____

10. mustard _____

Deep-Sea Details

Details are bits of information that go into more depth about a subject. Pay attention to the details as you read the passage.

In the deepest parts of the ocean, there is no light, no heat, and little food. There are, however, many kinds of living things! Their bodies have adapted to help them live in the deep, dark waters.

Most deep-sea animals don't chase their food. They save their energy by staying in one place, and they wait for food to sink down. Like many deep-sea fish, the dragon fish has a very big mouth to help it catch falling food. Some fish can actually make their own light to help them find food in the dark. A lantern fish has a body that lights up and very big eyes so it can easily spot food. Other deep-sea animals have no eyes at all. Sea spiders and basket stars live on the ocean floor, where there is nothing to see. They don't have eyes, but they do have long arms that help them move along the muddy ocean floor to find food.

Read each question. Circle the correct answer.

1. How do deep-sea animals get food?
   a. They chase fish and catch their food.
   b. The stay in one place and wait for food to fall.
   c. They search for plants they can eat.
   d. They use light to make their own food.

2. What does a dragon fish have to help it catch food?
   a. a big mouth
   b. long arms
   c. a big net
   d. light

3. How does a lantern fish see in the dark?
   a. It has a big mouth that lights up.
   b. It can see the sunlight with its big eyes.
   c. It has eyes that light up.
   d. It has big eyes and a body that lights up.

4. Which two deep-sea animals have no eyes?
   a. sea stars and basket spiders
   b. sea spiders and dragon fish
   c. basket stars and sea spiders
   d. lantern fish and dragon fish

Story Map

You can use a **story map** to organize information and details from a story.

Read the story and pay attention to what happens.

Laura carefully poured the cake batter into the pan while her sister Janelle opened the oven door. It was their mother's birthday, and they were baking a cake.

"Let's make her a big birthday card while the cake bakes," Laura suggested. The girls rushed off to their bedroom. Before long, paper, pens, and crayons were spread on the floor. They lost track of time until the phone rang loudly. The girls rushed back to the kitchen.

"Mom's going to be home any minute! We forgot about the cake!" Janelle shouted. While Laura answered the phone, Janelle pulled the smoking cake out of the oven. It was burned and smelled terrible.

"That was Mom on the phone," Laura said. "She's going to be home a little late, so we have time to make another dessert." In the pantry they found chocolate chips, sprinkles, and caramel. With the ice cream that was in the freezer, they could set up a sundae bar in the kitchen.

"We can still give her the card too!" Laura said.

"Yes," agreed Janelle, "and there's no way we'll burn the ice cream!"

Think about the cause and effect of each event in the story. Complete the story map.

Cause

Effect

Cause	Effect
1. It was Laura and Janelle's mom's birthday.	
2.	The cake burned.
3. Their mom was going to be home late.	

Splitting Up Sentences

Sentences can be split into a **subject** and a **predicate**.

For example: The students in the class   split up into two teams.
            simple subject   simple predicate

A simple subject has one noun. A **compound subject** has two or more nouns.
For example: Joyce and her twin sister   were on the blue team.
            compound subject   predicate

A simple predicate has one verb. A **compound predicate** has two or more verbs.
For example: The red team   got in line and put on red hats.
            subject   compound predicate

Read each sentence. Underline the subject and circle the predicate. Then check the correct subject column and the correct predicate column for each sentence.

	simple subject	compound subject	simple predicate	compound predicate
1. <u>Deon and Nick</u> were both on the blue team.		✓	✓	
2. The blue team hoped to win and practiced for a long time.				
3. The teacher blew her whistle and started the game.				
4. The red team and the blue team played their best.				
5. Everyone tried to score points to win the game.				
6. The teacher and her students came to the scoreboard.				
7. Deon and the rest of his team saw the scoreboard and cheered.				
8. The blue team scored the most points and won the game!				

Zoo Clues

As you read you may come across words that are new and unfamiliar. Look at other words and phrases that are built into the sentence. These **context clues** can help you figure out the word's meaning.

For example: The Zoo of the Canyons has many *native* animals that are from the local desert right in *this area*! *Native* means coming from the same place or area.

Where can people go to see animals up close and have fun? A zoo! But a zoo is much more than a fun amusement park. Zoos do important work helping animals in their homes, or habitats, outside of the actual zoo. There are certain groups of animals around the world that are dying out too quickly. If all the animals from the same group die, then that species will be gone from the earth forever. Zoo workers travel to other parts of the world to study animal groups that might die out and become extinct. Zoos try to help these endangered animals from becoming extinct by giving them a safer home. The animals can get stronger and have families. Once animals are out of danger and more stable, sometimes they leave the zoo and go back to the wild!

A lot of work goes on at a zoo to keep animals protected and unharmed. Zoos are not just about showing animals to people. They are for teaching people about how special and unique animals really are. The more people learn about animals, the more they can help, too!

Match each word with its meaning. Use context clues in the reading to help you. Write the letter on the line.

1. _____ amusement

2. _____ habitat

3. _____ species

4. _____ extinct

5. _____ endangered

6. _____ stable

a. out of danger and safe

b. a group of the same type of animal

c. an animal home

d. when an animal could become extinct

e. fun and enjoyment

f. no longer alive on the earth

Information Search

Headings can help you find information in a long passage. Think about where the information you're looking for might be.

Computer Lab

Computer Lab
The school's new computer lab is now open and has twenty-five computers and five printers. Some computers may be used for playing games or checking e-mail on the Internet.

After-School Classes
Each class is six weeks long:

Keyboarding
Mondays at 3:30 PM

Photo Books   *Computer Club*
Fridays at 4:00 PM   Wednesdays at lunchtime

Rules & Hours
There is no food or drink allowed in the computer lab. During open hours, students may visit the lab on their own.
Open Hours:
Before School: 7:30 – 8:00 AM
Recess and Lunch
After School: 2:30 – 4:00 PM

Check which section of the flyer has the information you're looking for.

	Computer Lab	Rules & Hours	After-School Classes
1. what time the lab is open before school			
2. when the computer club meets			
3. how many printers are in the lab			
4. if you can eat lunch in the lab			
5. how to sign up for the photo book class			
6. if the computers have Internet access			
7. how many weeks the after-school classes run			
8. the total number of computers in the lab			

Characters with a Cause

Characters have different **motives**, or reasons, for what they do.

Pay attention to the personality and the motives of each character as you read the story.

Jacob nearly dropped his boogie board when he stepped onto the bus and saw his classmate Miles sitting in the first seat. Jacob took the bus to the beach almost every Saturday, but he had never seen Miles there before. Miles just didn't seem like the kind of guy who would like the beach. Even now, his head was buried in a book.

"What's all this stuff for?" Jacob asked Miles. Miles had a big backpack full of test tubes and containers.

"It's for my science project," Miles explained. "I'm getting samples of the ocean water. This beach has been polluted before. People are trying new things to clean it up. I can test the water and see how clean it is."

"Wow," Jacob said. He had never thought about doing anything at the beach other than playing in the waves. "The cleaner the water is, the more I can enjoy it on my boogie board!"

"I bet you could use that board to get some great samples for me from the deeper water," Miles suggested.

"I can do that," Jacob agreed. "When you're done getting all your samples, you can take a ride on my board!"

Read each question. Circle the correct answer.

1. Miles is going to the beach to _____.
  a. show that people don't care about the water
  b. study and learn about the water
  c. keep people from swimming in the water
  d. collect sand for a project

2. Why does Jacob agree to help Miles?
  a. He feels sorry for Miles and wants to be friends.
  b. He decides that boogie boarding is silly and wants to do something important.
  c. He realizes that keeping the water clean will help him enjoy the beach.
  d. He wants to help Miles get done faster so he'll leave the beach.

Sentences Made Simple

A **simple sentence** has one subject and one predicate.

For example: <u>Homemade pizza</u> <u>is healthy and fun to make</u>.
   subject   predicate

A **compound sentence** is made of two sentences joined together.
It has two subjects and two predicates.

For example: <u>Homemade pizza</u> <u>is fun to make</u>, but <u>the dough</u> <u>can be tricky</u>!
   subject   predicate   subject   predicate

Read each sentence. Write *simple* or *compound*.

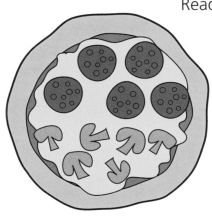

1. John sprinkled flour on the rolling pin and rolled out the pizza dough. _____

2. While the dough was rising, John made the tomato sauce. _____

3. The pot of sauce was bubbling, and a wonderful smell filled the room. _____

4. John spooned the sauce onto the dough and spread it around. _____

5. The cheese still needed to be grated, and the peppers needed to be diced. _____

6. Pepperoni, mushrooms, and onions were John's favorite toppings. _____

7. The pizza was finally ready, so John put the pizza inside the oven. _____

8. John and his family enjoyed eating the delicious pizza when it was done! _____

Paragraph Parts

A **paragraph** usually has a topic sentence, supporting details, and a concluding sentence. **Transition words** help link ideas together. All of the sentences in a paragraph talk about the same main idea.

For example: **Topic Sentence & Main Idea**   **Transition Words**

Autumn is a season filled with changes. To begin with, autumn marks the end of summer and the beginning of a new school year. The weather slowly changes from warm to cool. This shift in weather causes changes in nature. Leaves turn red and gold and fall off trees. Also, it gets dark earlier and the days get shorter. All of these changes are part of preparing for wintertime.

Concluding Sentence

Read each group of sentences. Number the sentences in the order that makes a logical paragraph.

A. _____ These students will get to help make decisions and plan school activities.

_____ The student council gives students a chance to be leaders.

_____ As students do these things, they learn leadership skills.

_____ Each class can choose two students to be part of the council.

B. _____ On the other hand, milk and juice cartons cannot be recycled because they have a waxy coating.

_____ So be sure to put recyclable paper and trash in the right place!

_____ You can recycle things like cardboard, paper bags, newspapers, and magazines.

_____ Most things made of paper can be recycled, but there are a few that cannot.

C. _____ The first group is usually called russet potatoes, which have thick brown skin.

_____ There are three main groups of potatoes.

_____ So, next time you eat a potato, try to figure out which group it belongs to!

_____ Finally, there are red potatoes, which are small and have very thin skin.

_____ White potatoes, on the other hand, are lighter on the inside and outside.

Wacky Weather

A **topic sentence** introduces the topic and the main idea.

Supporting details give more information about the topic.

The **concluding sentence** restates the main idea of the paragraph.

Pick a type of weather that you know about. Write a paragraph telling about it. Use the questions below to help you get started. Make sure your paragraph has all the parts.

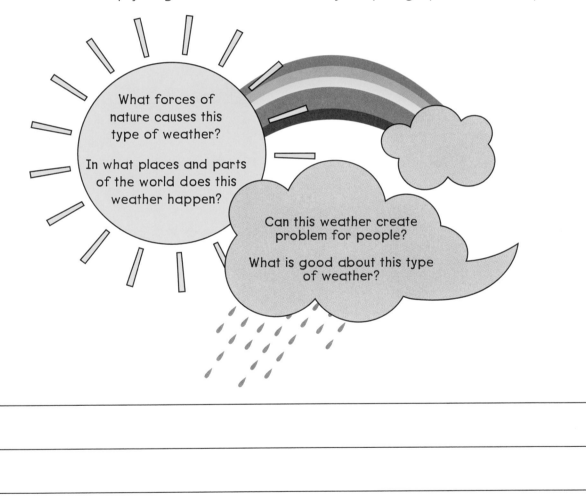

What forces of nature causes this type of weather?

In what places and parts of the world does this weather happen?

Can this weather create problem for people?

What is good about this type of weather?

_____

_____

_____

_____

_____

Word Parts Puzzle

Word endings can be added to words to change the meaning.

Add **–s**, **–es**, or **–ies** to show more than one.
    For example: baby   babies

Add **–d** or **–ed** to show past tense.
    For example: crawl   crawled

A **root word** is the base of the word when you take away prefixes and suffixes.
    For example:
    In the word *disappearing*, *appear* is the root word (dis<u>appear</u>ing).

Read the clue and complete the puzzle.

Across

1. root of the word *entertainment*
2. root of the word *copies*
3. root of the word *happiness*
4. root of the word *displaying*
5. root of the word *drainage*

Down

6. more than one beach
7. past tense of the word *trap*
8. root of the word *dancing*
9. past tense of the word *study*
10. root of the word *admitted*
11. root of the word *prepaid*

Prediction Pages

You can **predict** what a book or passage might be about just by reading a small part. Titles, topic sentences, and words give us clues about what's coming later.

Read what's inside each book. Complete each sentence with the best prediction.
Circle the correct answer.

1. *Skateboarding Tricks Made Easy*
This book will most likely explain _____.
a. where you can learn how to skateboard
b. how to trick people into buying a skateboard
c. where to buy a new skateboard
d. how to do flips on your skateboard

2. Skateboarding started in California in the 1940s. The rest of this paragraph will probably give details about
_____.
a. where to skateboard in California
b. different kinds of skateboards
c. the history of skateboarding
d. the biggest cities in California

Try making your own prediction. Read the topic sentence.
Then write what the rest of the paragraph is probably about.

3. It's unfair that kids cannot ride their skateboards to school.

_____

_____

_____

_____

_____

Stormy Simile Search

Writers use **figurative language** to describe things. A **simile** is a type of figurative language. Similes compare two things with the words *like* or *as*.

For example: *Thunder* pounded <u>like</u> a *drum*.
                    The *raindrops* seemed <u>as</u> big as *rocks*.

Read the passage. Find five similes and underline them. Remember, just because you see the word *like* or *as*, it doesn't mean it is a simile. A simile compares two things.

    I always like stormy weather. A big storm started last night just as I was falling asleep. First, I heard rain tapping on the roof like the sound of scampering mice. I went to the window and put my hand on the glass. The window felt as cold as ice. The temperature outside was dropping lower. As the storm went on, the rain became louder and louder. Soon, the wind howled like screeching tires. Trees swayed and branches snapped. The wind was like a giant rake, pushing and dragging leaves across the ground. And then the rain began to fade. Suddenly, it was as quiet as a library. The storm was over!

Complete each sentence with your own stormy similes.

1. During a storm, the sky is like a _____.

2. Raindrops are as _____ as _____.

3. Storm clouds are like _____.

4. Lightning is as _____ as a _____.

5. The fog covers everything like a _____.

Playing a Part

Words are divided into different groups, or **parts of speech**. These groups tell how words are used in a sentence. These are some of the groups:

noun: names a person, place, or thing

pronoun: a word that takes the place of a noun (*he*, *she*, *we*)

verb: an action word

adjective: a describing word

article: a small word used to introduce a noun (*the*, *an*)

Read each sentence. Write the part of speech for the underlined word.

1. Ruby is going to try out for the school <u>play</u>. _____

2. The play tells the story of people traveling on <u>a</u> boat. _____

3. Ruby wants to play the part of the <u>grumpy</u> ship captain. _____

4. <u>She</u> practices the lines at home with her mom. _____

5. Finally, it's time to say her lines on <u>the</u> big stage. _____

6. Ruby stands up tall and speaks her lines with a <u>loud</u> voice. _____

7. The teacher listens and <u>writes</u> down some notes. _____

8. The students have to wait a few days to see which part <u>they</u> will play. _____

9. Finally, the teacher posts a <u>paper</u> showing all the parts. _____

10. Ruby <u>smiles</u> widely because she got the part of the ship captain! _____

Pick a Prefix

| re– | pre– | dis– | un– | in– | im– | mis– |

Fill in the correct prefix to complete the word. You will use each prefix from above once.

1. Rachel was walking her little sister Allie to _____school.

2. They passed by a lovely garden filled with _____usual flowers.

3. Rachel stopped to look at the flowers, but Allie was _____patient.

4. She decided to _____behave by picking the prettiest flowers and putting them in her pocket.

5. "What you did was _____appropriate," Rachel told Allie.

6. The girls knew that it would be _____honest to take the flowers.

7. They decided to help the owner _____plant the flowers.

Read each definition. Add one of the prefixes above to write the word on the line.

8. to spell something wrong _____

9. not perfect _____

10. to count again _____

11. to take off a cover _____

12. to wash before _____

13. not complete _____

14. not to agree _____

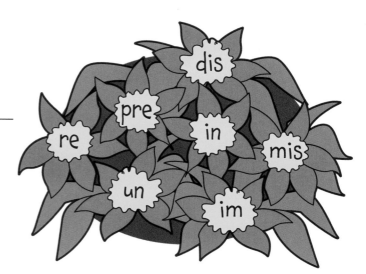

Fun with Foreshadowing

Sometimes authors give us hints about what might happen later in the story. This is called **foreshadowing**. It's like having a window to see ahead into the story. As you read the story, look for hints about what might happen later.

Emily pulled the blankets up to her chin and shivered. She could hear snow falling outside, and she knew she'd have to shovel the walk the next morning—again.

She even dreamed about snow that night! In her dream, she was digging in the snow when her shovel hit a big box. She opened the box and found an old scarf inside. It had been her favorite scarf because it was so warm. Emily was snuggling her face against her blanket when a trickling sound woke her up.

She saw water dripping off the icicles in her window. The sun was shining and the snow was melting! Emily raced outside to feel the warm sun on her face.

"Hello, Emily," a voice called out. Emily turned around to see Mr. Stevens, her neighbor. He had been away visiting his grandchildren for many weeks. Not only was Mr. Stevens back in town, he was shoveling the walkway to her house for her!

"I brought a friend back with me," Mr. Stevens said. Just then, a puppy bounded out of the house and raced toward Emily. She knelt down and he licked her hands.

Read each question. Circle the correct answer.

1. How does Emily's dream give a hint about what happens later in the story?

a. The old scarf is a hint that an old friend will be coming home.

b. The buried box is a hint that Emily has lost something important.

c. Emily's digging is a hint that she will have to shovel the walk the next morning.

d. All the snow in Emily's dream is a hint that things will never change.

2. When Emily wakes up, the snow is melting. The change in weather foreshadows how _____.

a. Mr. Stevens' puppy will bring more problems to the neighborhood

b. Mr. Stevens is lonely without his grandchildren

c. the neighborhood is changing into a dangerous place

d. the new puppy will be a happy change for Emily

Metaphor Match

A **metaphor** is a comparison between two things. It does not use *like* or *as*. A metaphor states that one thing is something else.

For example: My baby <u>sister</u> is a <u>feather</u>!
The comparison shows that her sister doesn't weigh very much.

<u>She</u> is a <u>ray of sunshine</u> for everyone.
The comparison shows that she brightens and cheers people up.

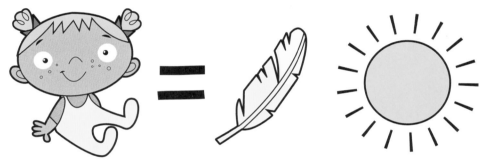

Read each metaphor. Underline the two things being compared. Then match the metaphor to the sentence that explains how the two items are alike. Write the letter on the line.

1. ___c___ <u>Dinnertime</u> at our house is a <u>race</u>.

2. _____ Today's homework is a piece of cake.

3. _____ Uncle Jim is a giant!

4. _____ After lunch, the kitchen was a disaster.

5. _____ These kids are wild animals.

6. _____ This week was a roller coaster.

7. _____ In the morning, my brother is a bear.

8. _____ Music class is always a party.

a. Both were unpredictable with ups and downs.

b. Both are restless and hard to control.

c. Both are done quickly.

d. Both are tall.

e. Both are easy to finish.

f. Both were messy and out of order.

g. Both are grumpy.

h. Both are lively and fun.

Vacation Verbs

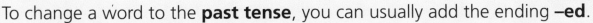

Make sure the subject of each sentence **agrees** with the verb.

For example: The *train leaves* at 10:00 AM and arrives at noon.
        The *trains leave* on time, so don't be late!

To change a word to the **past tense**, you can usually add the ending **–ed**.
For example: I *pack* my suitcase quickly.   I *packed* my suitcase quickly.

Some irregular verbs do not follow this rule.
For example: I *buy* my airline tickets online.   I *bought* my airline tickets online.

Complete each sentence. Circle the correct verb.

1. My family always _____ somewhere fun for summer vacation.
   travel   travels   traveling

2. Last summer we _____ a week in the mountains.
   spend   spent   spended

3. Whenever we travel, each person _____ his or her own luggage.
   carry   carries   carrys

4. Before we _____ on vacation, we always clean our house.
   leave   leaves   left

5. One summer, we _____ the perfect beach for camping.
   finded   found   founded

6. We _____ sand castles and swam in the ocean.
   builded   built   build

7. We listened to the waves at night as we _____ in our tent.
   sleep   sleeped   slept

8. Soon my dad will _____ a family meeting to plan our next vacation.
   holds   hold   held

Sunken Suffixes

A **suffix** is a word part added to the end of the word.

For example: hope + ful = hopeful   *full of hope*
               hope + less = hopeless   *without hope*

Sometimes two suffixes are used.
For example: hope + ful + ly = hopefully   *in a hopeful way*
               hope + less + ness = hopelessness   *the state of being without hope*

–ion	–less	–ly	–ness	–able	–ful	–en	–er

Fill in the correct suffix to complete the word in each sentence.
You will use each suffix from above once.

1. The underwater explor_____ was swimming in the deep ocean.

2. He shined a light to see through the dark_____.

3. Something sticking out of the sand was just barely notice_____.

4. It was an old, wood_____ treasure chest that had sunk to the ocean floor.

5. Inside the chest he saw sparkling, color_____ jewels.

6. He proud_____ brought the treasure chest back to land to show everyone.

7. The treasure was taken to someone for an inspect_____.

8. The jewels were all fake, so the treasure was worth_____!

Read each sentence. Find the word that has two suffixes and underline both suffixes.

9. There is a great peacefulness deep under the water.

10. Divers must swim carefully when they explore.

11. A diving suit and mask should fit comfortably.

12. Divers can follow a map so they
won't be directionless.

Clever Conclusions

A **conclusion** is a logical guess based on information.

For example:
The final baseball game of the season is this Friday night. Please join us for a party on Saturday afternoon. We will meet at Pinecrest Lake at 11:00 AM. Don't forget to bring your bathing suit!

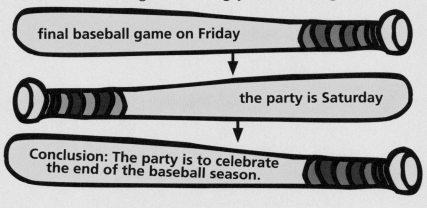

final baseball game on Friday

the party is Saturday

Conclusion: The party is to celebrate the end of the baseball season.

Read each passage. Underline the best conclusion.

1. Watering the lawn helps the grass stay green and healthy. The water needs time to sink down deep below the grass. If it's really hot outside, the water can dry up before it has time to sink in. It's best to water the lawn at the coolest time of the day.

   Watering the lawn wastes too much water during the summer.
   You should water the lawn in the early morning or the evening when it's cool.
   Watering the lawn in the middle of the day will help the grass stay green.
   You should leave the water on for a long time so it has time to absorb.

2. As soon as the bell rang, the students rushed inside and began putting their things away. The coat closet was usually open, but today it was still locked. That's when the class noticed an unfamiliar woman standing at the front of the classroom. On the chalkboard behind her it said, "My name is Mrs. Webster."

   It's the first day of school.
   There is something important locked in the coat closet.
   The school principal is visiting the classroom.
   The class has a substitute teacher for the day.

Tiger Finds a Teacher

Read the Chinese fable.

High in the mountains of China, there was a clumsy tiger. He had a hard time catching animals to eat because he could not climb up the mountainside without stumbling. One day, he noticed a cat climbing up the mountain swiftly. He asked the cat to teach him to climb.

"If I teach you," the cat said, "what's to stop you from catching and eating me?"

"I will not betray you," the tiger promised.

The cat thought this was a fair deal and believed the tiger. She began giving him climbing lessons, and soon she had taught him all her tricks except for one.

One day the cat looked so fat and tasty that the tiger's mouth began to water. The cat knew the tiger was up to no good and decided to give him a test.

"You don't need any more lessons," the cat said. "I've taught you all I know. If I have nothing left to learn from the cat, then I can eat her," the tiger thought to himself. He came up with a plan to fool her.

"Teacher, look at that tree!" the tiger cried, pointing to a tree. When the cat turned toward the tree, the tiger tried to eat her. But she was too fast for him, and she quickly climbed to the top of the tree. The tiger threw himself against the tree and tried to climb it. But the cat had never taught the tiger to climb trees.

Read each question. Circle the correct answer.

1. Why does the tiger need help from the cat?
   a. The tiger needs help learning how to climb trees.
   b. The cat is the only one who knows how to catch animals.
   c. The tiger is clumsy and wants to learn how to climb.

2. What is the lesson learned in this fable?
   a. Learning to climb is too difficult for some animals.
   b. A smaller animal can outwit a bigger animal.
   c. Always teach people everything you know.

The Ungrateful Tiger

Read the Korean fable.

One day, a traveler came upon a tiger that had fallen into a deep pit and was stuck.

"Kind traveler," the tiger said, "if you help me get out of this pit, I will reward you." The traveler believed the tiger would keep his word, so he lowered a tree branch into the pit. The tiger climbed out to safety.

"Now I am going to eat you up!" the tiger said to the traveler.

"You are so ungrateful!" the angry traveler said.

A wise toad crawled out from under a rock and agreed to help the tiger and the traveler settle their problem. The toad asked, "How did it happen? Show me where you were when the traveler came along."

"I was down in the bottom of this pit," the tiger explained. He jumped back into the pit to show the toad.

Just as the tiger jumped in, the traveler quickly pulled the tree branch out of the pit. The tiger roared with anger, as he was once again trapped at the bottom of the pit.

"You should be on your way," the toad said to the traveler. "In the future don't help such ungrateful creatures!"

Compare this fable with the one on page 28. Read each sentence. Check whether it describes "Tiger Finds a Teacher" or "The Ungrateful Tiger." If it describes both, check both columns.

	"Tiger Finds a Teacher"	"The Ungrateful Tiger"
1. Tiger takes lessons from a smaller animal.		
2. The fable has a human character.		
3. Tiger needs help from someone.		
4. Tiger is tested by another animal.		
5. Tiger does not keep his word.		
6. A smaller animal tricks a bigger animal.		

Plenty of Paragraphs

Saturday

Passages often have many paragraphs.

The first paragraph is usually the **introduction** paragraph. It sets up the main ideas and gets the reader's attention.

The **body paragraphs** are in the middle. They give more details and information about the subject.

The last paragraph is usually the **conclusion**. The conclusion restates the main ideas.

My Perfect Saturday

(1)　Bzzz! My alarm clock rings to wake me up for another long school day. If only today were Saturday, I think to myself as I yawn and stretch. If I could plan my perfect Saturday, I'd fill my day with my favorite things.

(2)　In the morning, I would sleep in as late as I could. I'd eat my delicious breakfast in my pajamas with my family. Then I would crawl back in bed and play video games.

(3)　My perfect afternoon would be filled with outdoor fun. I would pack a picnic lunch and head to the river. Then I would fish in the river with my dad.

(4)　To finish off my perfect Saturday, I'd have a movie night. I'd meet my friends at the movie theater and we'd have popcorn, hot dogs, and soda for dinner.

(5)　At the end of my perfect Saturday, I'd be tired out! Playing, fishing, and meeting friends at the movies would make for a busy and fun day. I'd drift off to sleep with a smile.

Answer the questions below.

1. Which paragraph is the introduction? _____

2. What is the topic of this passage? _____

3. What is paragraph 2 mostly about? _____

4. Which three paragraphs are the body paragraphs? _____

5. Which paragraph is the conclusion? _____

Super Saturday

Write your own passage about what you would do on your perfect Saturday. Make sure you include the following:

Introduction Paragraph: Get the reader's attention and introduce the topic.

Body Paragraphs: Give details about your topic. Make sure each paragraph has one main idea.

Concluding Paragraph: Restate the main topic.

Synonym Soup

Synonyms are two words that mean the same or almost the same thing.

For example: The soup was warm and <u>tasty</u>.
The broth was very <u>flavorful</u>.

Read each sentence. Circle the best synonym
  for the underlined word in the parentheses.

1. The chef had a special <u>method</u> for making
his soup.
(blender / technique / ingredient)

2. He always used a <u>medium</u> onion to give
the soup flavor.
(average / spicy / half)

3. The onion was <u>chopped</u> into tiny pieces.
(chewed / sharpened / diced)

4. He had a special spoon to <u>mix</u> all the ingredients together.
(tangle / shake / stir)

5. Eating this healthy soup is a great way to stay <u>skinny</u>.
(stout / light / slender)

6. The wonderful <u>scent</u> of the simmering soup filled the kitchen.
(smell / taste / spice)

7. The chef had to be <u>careful</u> with the boiling broth.
(sluggish / cautious / certain)

8. The soup was going to be served at a
fancy <u>banquet</u>.
(performance / feast / diner)

Delicious Directions

Read the butter-making directions.

What You Need

fresh cream	clear jar with a tight lid
salt	strainer
bowl	wooden spoon

Getting Ready

Before you begin, the cream needs to sit at room temperature for 12 to 24 hours. The cream will look shiny and taste a little sour when it is ready to be made into butter.

Making Butter

1. Put the cream into a jar and make sure the lid is tight.
2. Shake the jar for about 15 to 30 minutes. This shaking is called "churning."
3. When the cream starts to separate into buttermilk, it's time to stop shaking.
4. Pour the contents of the jar into a strainer. The buttermilk should drain out the bottom, and the lumps will be in the strainer. These are chunks of butter!
5. Gently rinse the butter chunks with cold water. Stir in a bowl and add salt.

Read each question. Circle the correct answer.

1. Why is the "Getting Ready" section important?
   a. It lists all the ingredients and tools you need to make butter.
   b. It shows you how to set up the kitchen for making your own butter.
   c. It explains what to do with the cream before you can start making butter.

2. It's time to stop shaking the jar when _____.
   a. the cream is at room temperature and looks shiny
   b. the butter is smooth
   c. the cream starts to separate and you see small lumps

3. Which step explains what "churning" is?
   a. Step 2
   b. Step 3
   c. Step 4

4. Which of the following tools is **not** needed to make butter?
   a. wooden spoon
   b. clear jar
   c. knife

A Personal Touch

Personification is giving an object or animal the qualities of a person. Verbs and adjectives can describe an object as if it were a human.

For example: The bright yellow <u>daisies welcomed</u> us to the garden. The verb *welcomed* shows how the daisies made the visitors feel welcome, just as a person would greet another person.

For example: A <u>shy rose</u> was hiding deep in the bushes. The word *shy* usually describes a quiet person who likes to stay out of sight, just like the rose in this sentence.

Read each sentence. Underline the words that show personification.

1. The leaves rustled as a light breeze whispered through the branches.

2. As the storm grew stronger, angry waves crashed on the shore.

3. We watched as cruel raindrops soaked our picnic blanket.

4. A plate of warm, soft cookies called out, "Eat me!"

5. Her grandmother's books were filled with photos that told stories about the past.

6. It was time to get rid of those tired shoes and throw them into the trash.

Complete each sentence. Use verbs or adjectives to personify the objects below.

7. It was a bright morning, and the sun _____.

8. The highway was crowded with _____ cars.

9. The sailboat raced along in the _____ wind.

10. During the blizzard, the snow _____.

All About Adverbs

Adverbs describe verbs. They tell when, where, and how things happen.

For example:
When: A package *arrived* at my doorstep *yesterday*.
Where: I *ran downstairs* to answer the door.
How: I *opened* the box up *excitedly*.

The verb is underlined in each sentence. Circle the adverb and check whether it describes when, where, or how.

	when	where	how
1. The mailman <u>knocked</u> (lightly) on the front door.			✓
2. I <u>will write</u> you a letter soon.			
3. We <u>walked</u> quickly to the mailbox.			
4. The mail often <u>arrives</u> in the afternoon.			
5. I carefully <u>stamped</u> each envelope before mailing it.			
6. The dog <u>barked</u> loudly at the mailman.			
7. You need <u>to send</u> that card today.			
8. The post office <u>closes</u> early on Saturday.			
9. Listen to the envelope <u>fall</u> down into the mailbox.			
10. A mail carrier <u>spends</u> most of the day outside.			

A Game of Opposites

Antonyms are two words that mean the opposite.

For example: *smooth* is the opposite of *rough*
                calm is the opposite of *excited*

Find a word that means the opposite for each word and write it into the puzzle.

Across

1. straight

2. sick

3. neat

4. rude

5. freeze

6. narrow

Down

7. disobey

8. friend

9. deep

10. future

11. thirst

12. sunset

Science & Sequence

As you read the passage, pay attention to the **sequence**, or order of events.

You can use a microwave oven to do everything from reheating pizza to boiling water. How did this amazing oven come about? It all started with a little bit of chocolate.

The year was 1946, and World War II had just ended. A scientist named Percy Spencer was walking through a science lab that made radar machines. The machines worked by sending out energy waves and seeing what they bumped into. When these "microwaves" bounced back, they showed if an enemy plane was flying nearby.

As Spencer walked by the machines, a chocolate bar in his pocket melted. He wondered if the microwaves in the machines could heat and cook other foods. He got a bag of popcorn kernels and placed it near the machine. Within moments, the kernels quickly exploded into fluffy popcorn.

The next day, Spencer brought an egg to the lab and put it near the machine. At first, nothing seemed to happen. Another scientist stepped closer to the egg to take a look. Suddenly, he had hot egg dripping from his face. The egg had gotten so hot that it exploded!

Spencer made an oven that used microwaves to cook food quickly and easily. The first microwave oven was over five feet tall and weighed 750 pounds! With time, he was able to make the oven smaller and less expensive. Years later, everyone was buying them!

Number the events in the correct order to show how Spencer invented the microwave oven.

_____ A chocolate bar in Spencer's pocket melted.

_____ Spencer put some popcorn kernels by the radar machine and they popped.

_____ Small microwave ovens were sold for people to use.

_____ It was after World War II, and Percy Spencer went into a science lab.

_____ Spencer walked by a radar machine that used microwaves.

_____ A raw egg was placed near the machine.

_____ A scientist stepped close to the egg and it exploded in his face.

_____ A 750-pound, five-and-a half-foot microwave oven was created.

Hyperbole Hunt

A **hyperbole** is an exaggeration. Writers use hyperbole to give their writing strong feeling.

For example: Sara told her mom <u>a thousand times</u> that she wanted a bike. The hyperbole shows that Sara told her mom over and over again. She didn't actually tell her mom one thousand times.

Read the story. Find five sentences that use hyperbole. Underline each hyperbole. Then write them on the lines below.

Our class wanted to help pick up trash at the park. Our teacher made a scavenger hunt game out of it. We were given a list that was a mile long! As we picked up trash, we needed to find the items on that list. Whoever could find all the items on the list first would be the winner.

I brought a bag to collect all the items on the list. In no time at all, I had found the first few things. My bag had a bottle, an old shoe, and a can. Pretty soon my bag was full and weighed a ton!

It was a hot day, and we all worked hard. Sweat dripped down my neck. I was being cooked alive! Finally, I found all the items on the list. I brought my bag to the teacher and won the scavenger hunt! At the end of the day, my feet were killing me. It was worth it, though. The park was clean once again!

1. _____

2. _____

3. _____

4. _____

5. _____

Preposition Party

A **preposition** is a connecting word. Prepositions help show the relationship between two things. A group of words that begins with a preposition is called a **prepositional phrase**.

For example: This invitation is _for a birthday party_.
                I'll bring a present _to the party_.

These are some prepositions:

for	in	to	at	on
of	with	during	before	around

Read each sentence and underline the prepositional phrase. Then circle the preposition.

1. This year, the big party was held at the park.

2. Some kids put their presents in pretty gift bags.

3. The weather was sunny and warm during the party.

4. All the kids sang "Happy Birthday" to the birthday girl.

5. We put the cake on a picnic table and cut pieces.

6. The birthday girl got the biggest slice of cake!

7. Kids enjoyed eating cake before the presents were opened.

8. Everyone went home with a fun party favor.

Complete each sentence with a prepositional phrase.

9. When I blew out the candles I wished _____.

10. There was a pile of presents _____.

11. I need to send thank-you cards _____.

12. It's fun to play party games _____.

In Other Words

A **thesaurus** is organized like a dictionary. It gives a list of synonyms for each word. Sometimes a thesaurus lists antonyms as well. You might use a thesaurus to:

find just the right word to express your idea
avoid repeating the same word
find a more interesting way to say something

tender *adj.*
1. soft, delicate
2. kind, loving, compassionate
3. gentle
4. painful, sore
(Ant.) rough, tough, thoughtless

stretch *verb*
1. reach, extend, spread, lengthen
2. prolong, drag out
3. overstate, exaggerate

stretch *noun*
4. area, space
5. length, duration

Replace the word *tender* in each sentence with an appropriate synonym.

1. After she tripped, her ankle was swollen and tender. _____

2. Casey picked up the baby puppy with a tender touch. _____

3. Rick wrote a tender message to his mother inside the card.

_____

Replace the word *stretch* in each sentence with an appropriate synonym.

4. Bend your legs and stretch your arms up high. _____

5. Nikki likes to stretch her bedtime for as long as possible. _____

6. During the final stretch of the race, everyone was cheering. _____

Popping the Question

One way of organizing ideas in a passage is to pose a question and answer it. The question usually introduces the topic and the passage that follows gives more details.

How Do Popcorn Kernels Pop?

Each popcorn kernel has a tiny amount of water in the center. When the kernel gets very hot, that water heats up. The pressure builds and the hot water needs to get out. The hard shell bursts open to let the steam out. A popped piece of popcorn is actually a popcorn kernel turned inside out!

Read each question. Circle the correct answer.

1. What is the main idea of this passage?

    a. A popcorn kernel has a hard shell with a tiny bit of water in the center.

    b. Popcorn kernels can only pop if they are in water.

    c. Popcorn kernels pop when the water at the kernel's center of a kernel gets hot.

2. The purpose of this passage is to _____.

    a. explain how a kernel of corn pops into popcorn

    b. convince people to pop their own popcorn

    c. inform people about how corn is grown to make popcorn

    d. warn people about the danger of popping corn

Read each short passage. Write a question to introduce it.

3. _____

Long ago, people used fire to make popcorn. They heated stones over a fire and then threw the kernels onto the stone. They also mixed kernels into hot sand and watched them pop.

4. _____

In addition to using butter and salt, there are many other tasty popcorn toppings. Seasoning or hot peppers can make spicy popcorn. Caramel, chocolate, and apple-cinnamon are toppings that can make sweet popcorn.

Figure It Out!

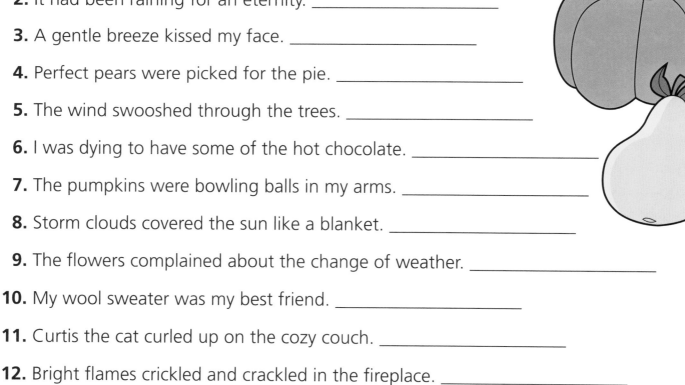

Writers use **figurative language** to bring their words to life. There are many different kinds of figurative language.

alliteration: a beginning sound repeated in several words
onomatopoeia: words that describe a sound
simile: a comparison using *like* or *as*
metaphor: a comparison linking two things
hyperbole: an exaggeration
personification: giving human qualities to objects or things

Read each sentence. Underline the words that use figurative language. Then write the type of figurative language it is on the line. There are two examples of each type listed above.

1. The autumn leaves were as red as apples. _____

2. It had been raining for an eternity. _____

3. A gentle breeze kissed my face. _____

4. Perfect pears were picked for the pie. _____

5. The wind swooshed through the trees. _____

6. I was dying to have some of the hot chocolate. _____

7. The pumpkins were bowling balls in my arms. _____

8. Storm clouds covered the sun like a blanket. _____

9. The flowers complained about the change of weather. _____

10. My wool sweater was my best friend. _____

11. Curtis the cat curled up on the cozy couch. _____

12. Bright flames crickled and crackled in the fireplace. _____

Join the Club!

A **conjunction** is a word like *and*, *or*, *so*, or *but* that joins groups of words together.

For example: Erin <u>and</u> Lisa are starting a chess club.
Kids who like chess <u>or</u> want to learn about it can join the club.

Two sentences can be joined together with a conjunction and a comma.
For example: The chess match is next week, <u>so</u> everyone needs to practice.
Erin has been playing chess for years, <u>but</u> Lisa is just learning.

Read each sentence. Underline the conjunction.
Some sentences might have more than one conjunction.

1. The first chess club meeting will be short and fun.

2. Kids will introduce themselves, so everyone can get to know each other.

3. Chess Club will meet in the library or at the lunch tables.

4. You can buy your own chess board and pieces, or you can use one from the club.

5. We will learn lots of chess drills, so you can learn how the game works.

6. You never know if you'll win or lose, so always try to have fun!

Complete each sentence with a conjunction.

7. Anyone can play in the chess match, _____ you must sign up in advance.

8. It takes concentration to play chess, _____ please be quiet when others play.

9. At the beginning of the game you must choose if you want to play the black _____ white pieces.

10. Both the king _____ queen pieces can move in any direction.

Sensory Search

A **narrative** is a personal story about something that happened to the writer. **Sensory details** can help a narrative come alive. These are details that appeal to the five senses: sight, taste, smell, touch, and sound.

Read the narrative. Underline examples of sensory details.
Then write one example for each sense below.

I had spent the whole afternoon doing yard work. My hands were raw and blistered from pulling so many weeds. My clothes smelled like fertilizer. I trudged inside and collapsed on the couch with a thud. My stomach growled so loud that my dad heard it across the room!

"You must be hungry," he said. "Let's go get a special treat."

I hopped into the car without even changing my dirty clothes. Finally, we pulled up in front of a little store with fancy letters on the window that said "Carla's Cupcakes."

As soon as I stepped inside, a sweet smell surrounded me. The counter had plates piled high with cupcakes of every kind! Chocolate, vanilla, lemon, and pumpkin were just a few of the cake flavors. The cakes were frosted in every imaginable color and topped with everything from sprinkles and chocolate chips to mints and marshmallows.

"I don't think I can choose just one!" I told my dad.

"You don't have to," he said. "We can buy a dozen and bring some home."

On the way home, I picked one of the cupcakes out of the box. It felt light and delicate in my hand. I'll never forget the first bite! The cake was moist and delicious. Sugary sprinkles melted in my mouth. Cleaning up the yard had been hard work, but the cupcakes made it worth it!

Sight _____   **Taste** _____

Smell _____   **Sound** _____

Touch _____

Good Night, Bad Night

Write your own personal narrative. Write about a night that was memorable to you.
You can choose if you want to write about one of your best nights, or one of your worst.
Make sure you use sensory details to make your narrative interesting.
Use the questions to help you get started and think of ideas.

What happened to make your night so memorable?

Where did you go?

What was the weather like?

What were you wearing?

Who was with you?

How did you feel?

_____

_____

_____

_____

_____

_____

_____

_____

_____

_____

_____

Words from Around the World

Read each question. Circle the correct answer.

1. Which word comes from the German word *selig,* which means "happy"?
   a. silly
   b. salty
   c. selfish
   d. segment

2. Which word comes from the Old English word *stol,* which means "throne"?
   a. stroll
   b. stale
   c. stole
   d. stool

3. Which word comes from the Middle English word *wealcon,* which means "to move about"?
   a. well
   b. wear
   c. walk
   d. whale

4. Which word comes from the Old English word *deor,* which means "dear"?
   a. door
   b. darling
   c. dare
   d. dread

5. Which word comes from the Norse word *sparkr,* which means "lively"?
   a. speck
   b. sprout
   c. sparkle
   d. spank

6. Which word comes from the Arabic word *qandi,* meaning "sugar"?
   a. candy
   b. quaint
   c. candle
   d. quad

7. Which word comes from the old French word *jangle,* which means "to chatter"?
   a. jungle
   b. juggle
   c. jagged
   d. jingle

8. Which word comes from the Dutch word *baas,* which means "master"?
   a. boss
   b. base
   c. bus
   d. boost

The Sky Is the Limit! Read me.

Some reading passages **compare and contrast** two things. The writer tries to show how the two things are similar and how they are different. As you read the passage, pay attention to what is being compared and contrasted.

Have you ever looked up in the sky and seen a message? You might have heard planes flying overhead as letters slowly appeared. There are actually two different ways for planes to put letters in the sky: skywriting and sky typing.

Skywriting is done by one plane that sends a trail of white smoke. The plane dips, swerves, and turns upside down to form each letter. It takes about 60 to 90 seconds to make one letter.

Sky typing is done with a team of five to seven planes. Each plane puts out small bursts of smoke to make dots in the sky. Within seconds, the dots blur together to form letters. It takes four seconds to make one letter.

Both skywriting and sky typing are good ways to get lots of people to see a message. The message in the sky can be seen for 15 to 30 miles in any direction, but both skywriting and sky typing fade after about 7 to 20 minutes!

Check whether each phrase describes skywriting or sky typing.
Sometimes both columns will be checked.

	skywriting	sky typing
1. done by one plane only		
2. fades after 7 to 20 minutes		
3. planes make dots of air that blur into letters		
4. people can see it 15 to 30 miles away		
5. takes about a minute to make one letter		
6. a trail of white smoke makes the letters		
7. is always done with a team of planes		
8. is a good way to get lots of people to see a message		

The Legend of Pegleg's Gold

A **legend** is a story that is usually about a person or place. The story is based on facts, but is often exaggerated or not completely true.

In the California desert there is a pile of rocks next to an old sign. The sign says, "Let those who seek Pegleg's gold add ten rocks to this pile." Who was Pegleg, and why are people still searching for his lost gold?

Back in the 1800s there was a man named Thomas Smith, who, after being shot in the leg, became known as "Pegleg." Once Pegleg got lost in a sandstorm in the desert. When he sat down to take a rest, he saw that a hill was covered with black rocks the size of walnuts. After stuffing his pockets with these strange black rocks, Pegleg found his way out of the desert.

He continued to the city, where he learned that the black rocks were actually gold! Many people went searching the desert for black gold, but nobody, including Pegleg, ever found it again!

Read each question. Circle the correct answer.

1. This story is a legend because _____.
   a. it is about a make-believe person named Pegleg
   b. nobody knows if Pegleg was a real person or if he was made up
   c. it is about a real person but some of the story may not be true

2. How did Pegleg get his name?
   a. He was shot in the leg and he got a wooden leg.
   b. He was a pirate searching for a lost treasure.
   c. He hurt his leg while he was lost in a sandstorm.

3. How did Pegleg find the black gold?
   a. He followed a map and it led him to the hills with black gold.
   b. He was on his way to the desert and he found a mine with black gold.
   c. He came upon a hill with black rocks when he was lost in the desert.

4. Why has nobody been able to find the place where Pegleg's gold came from?
   a. He hid the gold so others wouldn't be able to find it.
   b. He was lost in the desert when he found the gold.
   c. Since the gold looked like black rocks, nobody knew it was gold.

Cool Commas

Always use **commas** when writing dates, addresses, and locations, and to separate items in a list. You also use commas to set off groups of words in a sentence. An **appositive** is a group of words set off by commas that renames or identifies a noun.

For example: Powder Power, *the ski team at my school*, has practice on Saturdays.
Use two commas to set off an appositive in the middle of the sentence.

For example: *Open to skiers and snowboarders*, Frost Mountain is a great place to ski.
A comma comes after an appositive at the beginning of a sentence.

For example: It's always crowded in the cafeteria, *the warmest place in the ski lodge*.
A comma comes before an appositive at the end of the sentence.

Each sentence below is missing at least one comma. Add commas to make the sentences correct. Underline any appositives you see in the sentences.

1. My family likes to go skiing in Aspen Colorado.

2. Before playing in snow you should put on gloves boots, and a scarf.

3. Rock Canyon the park right by my house is a great place to go sledding.

4. You need patience determination and warm mittens to build a good snowman.

5. The biggest snowball fight happened on Saturday March 3.

6. Everything is on sale at the Snow Hut the best place to get skis sleds and skates.

7. December January and February usually get a lot of snowfall.

8. A dazzling performer on the ice the skater delighted the crowd.

Getting to the Root

Many of our **word roots** come from Greek and Latin. Once you know the meaning of the word root, it's easy to figure out the meaning of the whole word. The same roots appear in many different words.

Look at the word roots on the left below. Find two words in the tree that belong with each root. Not all of the words will be used.

aud _____

_____

form _____

_____

man _____

_____

pict _____

_____

brev _____

_____

scrib _____

_____

phon _____

_____

flex _____

_____

many   brief

abbreviation   auditorium

audible

script

manual   describe

picture   automobile

format   brave

reflex   reform

depict   telephone

flexible   phonics

photo   manage

aud: to hear   flex: to bend

form: shape   phon: sound

scrib: to write

man: hand   brev: short

pict: to show

Sorting Out Salt

A **graphic organizer** helps sort out information and ideas.

We use salt for so many things—from de-icing roads to flavoring French fries. Where does all the salt come from? It depends. Salt from different places is used in different ways.

Solar salt is salt from the ocean. Seawater gets trapped in shallow pools or ponds. Then the sun dries up all the water. Large, jagged mounds of salt are left behind. People put this solar salt in machines called "water softeners." These machines help make our water easier to use.

Evaporated salt comes from deep beneath the earth. Two tunnels are dug to reach the buried salt. Freshwater is blasted into the tunnel, and it breaks up the mound of salt. The salty water is then pumped up through the other tunnel. A special vacuum removes the water and leaves behind dry salt. This salt is used for baking and flavoring food.

Rock salt comes from underground mines. Miners use explosives to shake big chunks of salt loose. The large rocks of salt are sent up to the surface in elevators. After it's crushed down, rock salt is often used to melt ice on roads.

Complete the chart below.

	solar salt	evaporated salt	rock salt
1. Where is it found?	ocean water		
2. How is it made?	sun and wind dry up pools of water		
3. What is it used for?			

Mood Match

Mood is the feeling that a piece of writing has. The setting of a story, the character's actions, and other details help create the mood.

For example: *The rain pounding at the window woke Melissa up. It was a dark, gray morning and her feet were already cold.*
This passage creates a gloomy mood.

For example: *Sunshine gently lit up Melissa's room and nudged her awake. It was a bright, clear morning and she could smell eggs cooking for breakfast.*
This passage creates a cheerful mood.

Read each group of sentences. Write what type of mood it creates. Use the words in the word bank.

creepy	exciting	angry	hopeful	carefree	lonely

1. The stairs creaked as the boy crept down into the damp cellar. Dark shadows lurked on the walls and a chill went up his spine. _____

2. Leila wrote down her deepest wish and attached it to a white balloon. She smiled as she watched the balloon gracefully glide up to the sky, like a perfect cloud. _____

3. An empty swing swayed back and forth in the breeze. The playground was deserted, and Jacob sat quietly at the bottom of the hard slide. _____

4. As soon as the cage door clicked shut, Rover's eyes shone with rage. The whole cage shook as he growled and barked. _____

5. The warm breeze tickled Nikki's ears as she pedaled her bike through the park. She giggled when her hat flew off and landed in a tree. _____

6. The coaster clinked and clanked as it climbed to the top of a steep hill. Brenda's heart raced and she squeezed her eyes shut as the coaster plunged downward. _____

Putting It Together

Sentences can be combined to help link ideas together. There are many ways to **combine sentences**.

Use conjunctions like *and*, *but*, *or*, or *since*:

Jason wants to build a go-cart. He can't do it alone.
Jason wants to build a go-cart, *but* he can't do it alone.

Use commas to make an **appositive**:

Marvin is Jason's favorite cousin. Marvin helps Jason build the go-cart.
Marvin, *Jason's favorite cousin*, helps him build the go-cart.

Put all the details in one sentence:

Jason needs wheels for the go-cart. There should be four wheels made of metal.
Jason needs *four metal wheels* for the go-cart.

Read each set of sentences. Combine them into one by using a conjunction, writing an appositive, or combining details. Write the new sentence on the line.

1. Jason finds a plank of wood. The plank is too long for the go-cart.

_____

2. Marvin has experience using tools. Marvin helps cut the wood.

_____

3. Jason and Marvin sand the wood. They paint it black.

_____

4. They attach the wheels. The wheels are taken from an old baby stroller.

_____

5. Now it's time to attach a seat. The seat is soft and comfortable.

_____

6. Foster Park is the best place for go-carts. This is where Jason takes his first ride.

_____

Word Part Chart

Many **prefixes** come from Greek and Latin. Knowing the meaning of these word parts can help you figure out the meaning of the word.

For example: uni + cycle = unicycle
Uni– means "one" and _cycle_ means "circle" or "wheel." A unicycle is a one-wheeled bike.

auto–	self	**trans–**	over / across
inter–	between	**uni–**	one
micro–	small	**semi–**	half
multi–	many	**bio–**	life

Divide each word into parts. Use the chart to help write a definition for the word.

1. transport: <u>to carry over or across</u>

2. interlace: _____

3. uniform: _____

4. biology: _____

5. automobile: _____

6. international: _____

7. biography: _____

8. microscope: _____

9. multipurpose: _____

10. semicircle: _____

11. multipart: _____

12. semisweet: _____

Food Facts or Opinions

A **fact** states something that is proven to be true.

An **opinion** tells what someone thinks.

For example: Fact: *Oranges and strawberries have vitamin C.*
Opinion: *Oranges taste better than strawberries.*

Read each sentence. Write *fact* or *opinion*.

1. Cheddar, Swiss, and mozzarella are all types of cheese. _____

2. It takes about seven minutes to bake a potato in the microwave. _____

3. Pepperoni is the best pizza topping. _____

4. Wheat bread has more fiber in it than white bread. _____

5. Vegetables taste good when they are stir-fried or steamed. _____

6. Mayonnaise is made out of eggs, oil, and vinegar. _____

7. A peanut butter and jelly sandwich is easy to make and very filling. _____

8. Fish is too salty to eat in the morning. _____

Now write two facts and two opinions about hamburgers.

9. _____

10. _____

11. _____

12. _____

What Makes a Myth?

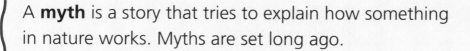

A **myth** is a story that tries to explain how something in nature works. Myths are set long ago.

Why the Frog Croaks

Long ago, the days and the nights had no pattern. The animals wanted to talk to Sun about making day and night more balanced. First, Bear and Frog would talk with everyone about their ideas. Then the animals would vote.

Bear wanted one long day and one long night. Bear was a bully and growled at each animal he spoke with. "Six months day and six months night," he snarled at Fox, Owl, and Fish. Then he went off to take a long nap.

Frog was friendly and hopped around to each animal, asking Fox, Owl, and Fish if they wanted longer or shorter days and nights. Frog agreed with them that shorter days and nights seemed to make sense.

It was time for Frog and Bear to report back to the animals, but Bear couldn't be found! He had been so sure that the other animals would vote for his idea, he didn't even bother to wake up from his nap to come to the meeting! They voted for Frog's idea, and they sent Eagle to tell Sun what they wanted. Sun agreed to divide the days and nights into the lengths that we know today. This is why you can now hear Frog croaking, "One day, one night," as he hops through the forest.

Answer the questions below.

1. How did Frog think day and night should be divided?

_____

2. How did Bear think day and night should be divided?

_____

3. How did Frog and Bear treat the animals differently?

_____

4. What did the animals decide about day and night?

_____

More Myths

This is a Native-American myth from the Creek tribe.

Origins of Day and Night

Long ago the animals met to talk about how day and night should be divided. Some animals wanted the day to last all the time. Others wanted night to go on forever. The animals argued about what to do. Then the Squirrel spoke up.

"Look at Raccoon's tail," Squirrel said. "The rings on his tail are divided equally between light and dark. First there is a light ring, then a dark one. Day and night should be divided like Raccoon's tail."

The animals thought Squirrel was very wise and decided to follow his idea. They divided day and night into equal parts, repeating over and over like the rings.

Bear was jealous that Squirrel was so wise. He scratched Squirrel's back with his long claws. To this day, Squirrel has a long stripe on his back.

Answer the questions below.

1. Why were all the animals arguing about day and night?

_____

2. What did Squirrel point out about Raccoon's tail?

_____

3. How did the animals decide to divide up day and night?

_____

4. How did Bear hurt Squirrel?

_____

5. How does this myth compare with "Why the Frogs Croak" on the previous page?
   a. Day and night are divided up evenly.
   b. The animals in each agree about how long day and night should be.
   c. Bear gives the wisest answer.

6. How does Bear behave in both of the stories?
   a. He listens carefully to all the other animals.
   b. He is sleepy and just wants to take a nap.
   c. He is a bully and is mean to others.

All About Jaguars

A **report** gives information about a topic or issue. It usually has an introduction paragraph, a few body paragraphs, and a concluding paragraph.

This is a student's report about jaguars.

(1)   Jaguars are amazing and strong animals. Learning about where jaguars live, how they look, and what they eat helps us understand why they are so special.

(2)   Jaguars are good swimmers and like to live near water. So rainforests, swamps, and wetlands are ideal homes for jaguars. They can also be found living in grasslands and even the desert.

(3)   These large cats grow to be about five to eight feet long. They have very sharp teeth. The yellow-brown coat of a jaguar is covered with black spots. These spots help it hide in the forest.

(4)   Jaguars can eat just about any other animal. Instead of chasing their prey, jaguars hide and wait for animals to pass by. Then they pounce on the animal in a surprise attack!

(5)   From the grasslands of Mexico to the rainforests of Brazil, jaguars rule the land. It's no wonder that long ago people worshipped the jaguar as a symbol of power!

Read each question. Circle the correct answer.

1. Which three subjects about jaguars are covered in this report?
   a. habitat, personality, and speed
   b. habitat, appearance, and diet
   c. rainforests, diet, and symbols

2. Where would this sentence best fit?
   Jaguars will eat anything from a small mouse to a big horse.
   a. paragraph 2
   b. paragraph 3
   c. paragraph 4

3. Which sentence from the report is a topic sentence?
   a. Then they pounce on the animal in a surprise attack!
   b. These spots help it hide in the forest.
   c. Jaguars can eat just about any other animal.

Animal Report

Choose an animal you know a lot about. Use the questions below to write some facts about your animal. Then use those notes to write a report on another piece of paper. Don't forget to include an introduction and a conclusion! You may need to look in some books or online to get more information to complete your report.

My Animal:

I. Where does it live?

II. What does it look like?

III. What does it eat?

Other interesting facts:

Many Meanings

Some words have more than one meaning.

For example: Weigh the box on the *scale*.
scale: a device that shows how much something weighs

The lizard has a spot on this *scale*.
scale: the thin, bony plates that make up the skin for some animals

Read each sentence. Circle the sentence below it that has an underlined word with the same meaning.

1. The water was warm and <u>clear</u>.
   a. Please <u>clear</u> all the trash out of the yard.
   b. It was <u>clear</u> that the puppy was excited.
   c. Drink only <u>clear</u> liquids for three days.

2. This green dress will <u>suit</u> you nicely!
   a. You need four cards of the same <u>suit</u> for this game.
   b. My mom wears a <u>suit</u> to her office each day.
   c. Let's pick a team uniform that will <u>suit</u> everyone.

3. Please help me <u>crack</u> this nut open.
   a. The baby chicks are ready to <u>crack</u> out of their shells.
   b. Leave the door open just a <u>crack</u>.
   c. Let's follow the clues and <u>crack</u> the case.

4. You can lick the <u>batter</u> out of the bowl.
   a. Pour the <u>batter</u> into two cake pans.
   b. The storm will <u>batter</u> the tent.
   c. The next <u>batter</u> hit a home run.

Cause & Effect

As you read the story, think about what happens **(effect)** and why **(cause)**.

Lisa's family was getting ready to send out holiday cards. They decided to have a photo taken of the whole family to put in the card.

"Look!" Lisa's mom said. "I got matching sweaters for everyone to wear in the photo!"

"I see one for me, you, and Dad—but what about Rex?" Lisa asked.

"I wasn't planning on having our dog in the photo," her mom explained.

"But Rex is part of our family!" Lisa said.

Lisa's mom agreed that Rex should be in the photo. After searching for something Rex could wear to match with the sweaters, they found a cute little dog hat.

When it came time to take the photo, Rex was so excited that he could hardly sit still. Lisa and her parents couldn't stop laughing. The photographer had to take a lot of shots!

Lisa and her mom chose their favorite picture to mail out with their holiday cards. Everyone who received a card loved the picture.

Read each group of sentences. Write which is the *cause* and which is the *effect*.

1. Lisa's family was going to take a family photo. _____

Lisa's mom bought matching sweaters. _____

2. Lisa and her mom found a hat for their dog, Rex. _____

Lisa convinced her mom to include the family dog in the photo. _____

3. The photographer took many different pictures of the family. _____

Rex was restless and made the family laugh during the photo session. _____

Fun with Fairy Tales

Fairy tales are stories written for children. They usually have magical creatures, monsters, princesses, or princes as characters.

Read this fairy tale from Russia.

Once there was a king in Siberia who had a daughter named Altyn-Aryg. He said to the queen, "I am getting old and we have no son. There is no one to look after all the people and the cattle when I die.

Altyn-Aryg overheard her father and stepped forward. "Father," she asked, "why can't I be the next ruler?"

"It is too great a task for a maiden," the king said.

Altyn-Aryg was very upset and decided to leave the kingdom. Her father gave her his sword before she left. In her travels, Altyn-Aryg slayed a terrible monster called the Snake Prince, freeing all the villagers trapped inside of him. Everyone shouted for joy. Many of the people and their cattle went with Altyn-Aryg. She returned home and told her father of how she killed the Snake Prince using his sword.

"It was brave of you. Now, I will give you the people and animals of this kingdom," he said. Soon after, the king died, and Altyn-Aryg became the next ruler.

Answer the questions below.

1. Why did the king think that Altyn-Aryg could not be the next ruler?

_____

2. How did Altyn-Aryg kill the Snake Prince?

_____

3. Why did the king finally decide to let Altyn-Aryg be the next ruler?

_____

4. Why is this story considered a fairy tale?

_____

Catch That Quote!

We use **quotation marks** and commas to set off a speaker's exact words. Always put punctuation marks inside the quote marks.

For example: My mom reminded us, "Shut the door quickly so the puppy doesn't get out!"

For example: "We'll be careful," my sister Denise said to Mom.

Read each sentence. Add quotation marks, commas, and punctuation marks to show the speaker's exact words.

1. The puppy ran out the front door my sister yelled.

2. As I ran out the door I yelled back We have to catch him quickly

3. He's getting away Denise said in a panicked voice.

4. I have an idea I said. Let's split up and try to corner him.

5. Denise agreed and said I'll go to the right and you go to the left

6. Look I said the puppy is in Mrs. Howard's garden

7. I hope he doesn't trample on her flowers Denise said

8. We've almost got him I said as we crept closer.

9. Gotcha Denise yelled as she scooped the puppy up into her arms.

10. We both hugged the puppy and I said I knew we could catch him

Making Sense of Sayings

Idioms are sayings that have a special meaning. If you take the phrase word for word, it won't make sense! You can use context clues to figure out the meaning of an idiom.

For example: Nora's shoelaces got caught in the wheel of her bike. She was really <u>in a pickle now</u>!

The idiom "in a pickle" doesn't mean that Nora is actually inside a pickle. It means that she's in a tricky situation.

Read each group of sentences. Circle the correct meaning for the underlined idiom.

1. It took a long time to find a parking spot and the movie was about to start. We made it inside just <u>in the nick of time</u>.
   a. earlier than everyone else
   b. right before time is up
   c. after it was too late

2. For years, Jerome would never eat his vegetables. Then, <u>out of the blue</u>, he started snacking on carrots and celery all the time!
   a. seemingly from nowhere
   b. very quickly
   c. without being asked to

3. My sister woke me up and told me it was snowing. When I looked out the window I remembered that it was summer time! She was just <u>pulling my leg</u>.
   a. calling me names
   b. dragging me out of bed
   c. playing a joke

4. Mason wanted to be on the soccer team, take piano lessons, and train for a race. "Be careful not to <u>bite off more than you can chew</u>," his mom said.
   a. do more than you can handle
   b. eat too much before you exercise
   c. put too much food in your mouth

5. Nick gave his little brothers some finger paint. When they started painting on the walls, Nick realized he'd <u>opened up a can of worms</u>.
   a. given his brothers too much to do
   b. opened up too many paint bottles
   c. started a bunch of new problems

6. Yumi and Jenny are <u>joined at the hip</u>. They are best friends and go everywhere together!
   a. holding hands
   b. always together
   c. have the same opinions

Purpose Pairs

Here are three purposes for why an author may choose to write something:

Inform: to give facts and information to a reader
Bread dough must rest and rise for several hours before baking.

Persuade: to convince the reader to think or do something
At Brenda's Bakery you can buy delicious, fresh loaves of bread at a good price.

Entertain: to tell an interesting story to the reader
Mary's face was covered in flour as she tried rolling out her bread dough.

Read the sentences or book titles and decide the author's purpose:
to *inform*, to *persuade*, or to *entertain*. Write the purpose on the line.

1. To play the game Head of the Class, you need four people. Each player starts out with his or her marker on the game board. Roll the dice to see who goes first.

_____

2. Buy backpacks, tents, hiking shoes, and more. No matter how wild your adventure is, our store has the right gear!

Adventure Gear ON SALE!

_____

3. Join hockey fans at the rink this Saturday for the first game of the season. It will be a great game! You can buy discount tickets this week. Don't miss out!

_____

4. Hikers often feel short of breath as they hike higher. There is less oxygen the higher up you go. Most hikers begin to get short of breath at around 5,000 feet.

_____

5.

The Goblin Gamekeeper

_____

6. As the group followed the trail across a meadow, they heard rustling in the bushes. It sounded like a bear was coming near them. Each hiker stopped and stood perfectly still in the cold water.

_____

Fast Fantasy

Fantasy is a type of story or genre. Fantasy stories have elements that are make-believe or impossible, such as talking animals or magical powers.

"Can I buy these shoes?" Erik asked his mom. They were browsing at a garage sale and Erik found a pair of shiny, yellow sneakers. He had never seen anything like them before. His mother agreed.

Erik was so excited after he bought the shoes, he put them on right away. Erik's feet tingled inside his new sneakers. Before he knew it, he was running! Erik and his sneakers finally came to a stop in front of his house, but Erik hadn't even broken a sweat. The shoes did all the work!

Erik's mother was very angry that he had taken off so fast. Erik took off his shoes and decided to take them back to the garage sale.

When he found the right house, the man who had sold him the shoes wasn't there. Erik asked the woman there if he could return the shoes. "I've never seen those sneakers before in my life!" she said. "You didn't buy them at our garage sale."

Erik looked down at his magic yellow sneakers. He wondered what kind of adventures they might have together.

Read each question. Circle the correct answer.

1. At the beginning of the story, Erik notices that the shiny sneakers were like nothing he had ever seen before. This is an example of _____.
   a. foreshadowing
   b. metaphor
   c. setting
   d. flashback

2. Why is this story a fantasy?
   a. The story is set at a spooky garage sale.
   b. The story is about sneakers with magical powers that make Erik run fast.
   c. Erik and his mother are the main characters and the story is set in the present time.
   d. In the story Erik upsets his mother and must find a way to solve his problem.

Mine, Yours, and Ours

To show that something belongs to a person, add an **apostrophe** and **–s** or use the **possessive pronoun**.

For example: This belongs to Betsy. The backpack is *Betsy's*.
This belongs to her. The backpack is *hers*.

Pronoun	Possessive
me	mine
you	yours
him	his
her	hers
us	ours
them	theirs

Complete each sentence with the correct possessive word. Use the chart above to help you.

1. I saw Brad wearing that hat earlier today. It's _____ hat.

2. Please take this notebook home with you. It's _____.

3. This wagon actually belongs to the family down the street. It's _____.

4. Heather returned the sweater to Angela. It was _____ sweater.

5. I won first place in the chess competition. The trophy is _____!

6. We brought this shovel to the park with us. It's _____.

7. I lent some of my video games to Paul. Now they are at _____ house.

8. I gave him back his colored pencils. The pencils are _____.

Hiding Homonyms

Homonyms are words that sound the same but are spelled differently. The words have different meanings as well.

For example:

The baby *bawled*.

The baby is *bald*.

Read each sentence. Underline the pair of homonyms.

1. All the kids know that there is no food allowed in the living room.

2. Always wear a pair of gloves before going to the pear tree to pick fruit.

3. The bruise on your heel will take about three weeks to heal.

4. I would accept your invitation to play, except I have piano practice.

5. If you pay a small fare the bus will take you to the front entrance of the fair.

6. Everyone stares at my sister when she comes down the stairs with a crazy hairdo.

7. As the mechanic fixed the brake pedal, I waited in the break room.

8. Over the weekend I will be as busy as a bee!

Complete each sentence. Circle the correct word in parentheses.

9. Bring a sack lunch on the field trip, and a sweatshirt (to / two / too).

10. I'm not sure (witch / which) pencil is mine.

11. Please put all homework in that tray over (they're / their / there).

12. If you eat a healthy dinner, then (your / you're) going to get dessert.

Tasty Titles

Titles of books, magazines, and newspapers are capitalized and underlined. On a computer, titles are put into italics instead of underlined.

For example: I checked out the book <u>Baking Basics</u> so I can learn to bake.

Did you see that recipe in <u>Kids Cooking</u> magazine?

There was an article about a new ice cream shop in the *Grayson City Gazette*.

Read each sentence. Circle the sentence if it has the correct capitalization and punctuation. If the sentence is incorrect, fix it.

1. I found a coupon for the new pizza place in the *Mayfield Times*.

2. In this issue of <u>Mountaineer Magazine</u>, there is an article about mountain bikes.

3. There are six kids on the waiting list to check out the book Palm Tree Paradise.

4. I found an old copy of Little red riding hood at a used bookstore.

5. This month I read about how to recycle in a magazine called <u>green kids</u>.

6. If I don't know a word, I look up the definition in the <u>Word Master Dictionary</u>.

7. I always check the classified ads in the <u>Crescent City</u> *Chronicle*.

8. Kids can send in their own jokes to be published in <u>Kidding Around Magazine</u>.

Something Fishy Is Going On

When you're doing research, it's important to gather lots of information. Imagine that you're researching careers working with fish. Pay attention to the information as you read.

At aquariums there are all sorts of interesting jobs for people who love fish. Designers work on building tanks and exhibits. Researchers study the fish in the aquarium and in the wild. Teachers help visitors learn about the fish they are seeing. And people called "aquarists" take care of the fish.

The aquarists work up close with the fish and other sea animals in an aquarium. Aquarists get to help feed the fish and make sure they are healthy. They also check everything in the tank, like filters, pumps, and water flow. Many aquarists get to work with the visitors and answer their questions.

One of the most important parts of an aquarist's job is to keep a close eye on the water. Sea animals are used to living in the salty ocean water. The saltiness of the water is called the salinity level. Aquarists spend a lot of time checking the salinity of the water in each tank. They make sure it's just right for the fish.

There is a lot of work that goes on behind the scenes at aquariums!

Read each question. Circle the correct answer.

1. This passage has information about all of the following except _____.

   a. a career as an aquarist
   b. aquarium history
   c. jobs at an aquarium

2. Which aquarium job lets you work on putting together exhibits and tanks?

   a. designer
   b. teacher
   c. aquarist

3. Why is the salinity level of water important?

   a. It tells how much oxygen is in the water.
   b. It shows how dirty the water is.
   c. It shows how much salt is in the water.

4. This passage would be most helpful for a student who _____.

   a. is writing about aquarium careers, especially an aquarist
   b. is researching different kinds of fish
   c. is gathering information about visiting a local aquarium

Fascinated with Fish

Articles and interviews are good sources of information. Read the interview below.

Career Connection brings you an up-close interview with Nelson Green, who works as an aquarist at Bolton City Aquarium.

CC: Describe your typical day.

Nelson: I check the salinity level, the temperature, and the flow of the water in the morning. I clean out any food that wasn't eaten. At lunchtime, I feed the fish. In the afternoon I help out with tours. Then at the end of the day, I count all the fish and fill out paperwork.

CC: What did you do to prepare for a career as an aquarist?

Nelson: In school I was always interested in the ocean and fish. I did a summer program at my local aquarium. Then in college I took lots of science classes like marine biology and oceanography. I volunteered at an ocean research station and I learned how to scuba dive. After college, I was very lucky to get this job!

CC: What the best part and worst part about being an aquarist?

Nelson: The best part is working with these amazing animals. My least favorite thing is cleaning out the tanks. But it's an important part of the job!

Compare this interview with the passage on page 70. Check whether each phrase describes the passage or this interview. If it describes both, check both columns.

	Passage	Interview
1. gives details about the job of an aquarist		
2. gives opinions about working with fish		
3. lists many jobs at an aquarium		
4. explains how to become an aquarist		
5. talks about the salinity of water in a tank		

Tattle Tales

This is a student's report about a book she read. The report tells about the plot, setting, characters, theme, and her favorite part of the story.

Charlotte's Web by E.B. White

(1)   Charlotte's Web is a book about a pig and the friends who help save his life. The story takes place on a farm. A little girl named Fern lives on the farm and convinces her dad not to kill the "runt." She names him Wilbur.

(2)   Wilbur soon learns that he is going to be killed and eaten in a few months. His new friend Charlotte, a spider, helps save him. She spins words into her webs that make Wilbur famous. Charlotte's plan works, and Wilbur is not killed.

(3)   My favorite part about this book is the character Templeton the rat. He is greedy and rude, and he always made me laugh. He is selfish, but he also helps Wilbur.

(4)   One theme of this book is friendship. Charlotte and Fern prove their friendship to Wilbur in many ways. The story shows that something small, like a spider and some simple words, can have a big effect.

Read each question. Circle the correct answer.

1. Paragraphs 1 and 2 do all of the following **except** _____.

   a. describe some of the characters

   b. tell about the theme

   c. explain the setting

2. The author's favorite thing about the book is _____.

   a. the words written into the web

   b. the character Templeton

   c. the friendship between the characters

3. The purpose of the fourth paragraph is to _____.

   a. explain the book's theme

   b. explain the ending of the book

   c. tell why others should read the book

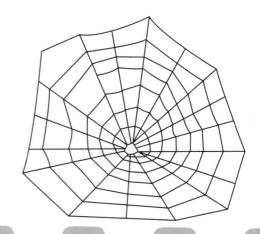

Read and Report

Write your own report about a book you've read. Use the questions to get started. Then write your report on the lines below.

Who are the main characters in the story?

What is the setting?

What are the most important things that happen in the story?

What is your favorite part?

Would you recommend this book to a friend?

Uncover the Compound

When two words are put together, they form a **compound word**.

For example: pan + cake = pancake

Read each sentence. Circle the compound word.

1. The preschool has a lovely courtyard where the children can play.

2. After a sleepless night, the doctor gave Ben some medicine for his headache.

3. Our neighbor shows her kindness by shoveling snow off our sidewalk.

4. Some of the words were misspelled in the paper's headline.

5. It was such a windy day that Sara had to redo her ponytail many times.

6. The candy machine was filled with colorful gumballs in every size imaginable.

Think of as many compound words as you can that go with each word below. The word can be first or last in the compound word.

water

waterfall

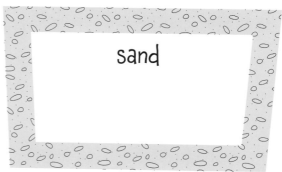

sand

butter

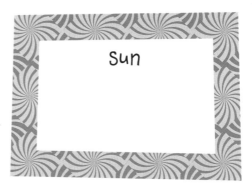

sun

From Trash to Treasure

Some pieces of writing try to explain an opinion or idea to the reader. This pattern is called **proposition and support**. The writer proposes an idea and then gives facts and details to support it.

This passage was written by a student. He wants to propose an idea for his school. As you read, think about his idea and how he supports it.

(1)   From lunch scraps to computer paper, our school makes a lot of trash every day! Where does it all go? We already throw some of our trash into recycling bins. But we can do more. Our school should begin a composting program.

(2)   Compost looks like a pile of crumbly soil. It's made of plants like dead leaves, grass clippings, and weeds. Some kinds of food, like fruit and vegetables, can also be part of the pile. All the stuff in the pile starts to decompose, or break down. This is nature's way of returning nutrients back to the earth.

(3)   Composting would teach students at our school a lot about science. Students could take turns mixing or "turning" the pile. We could keep track of the temperature and measure the moisture. This would be a hands-on way to learn about recycling.

Read each question. Circle the correct answer

1. Which sentence gives the author's proposal, or idea?
   a. Composting would teach students at our school a lot about science.
   b. From lunch scraps to computer paper, our school makes a lot of trash every day!
   c. Our school should begin a composting program.

2. The purpose of paragraph 2 is to _____.
   a. explain what compost is
   b. present the main proposal about a compost program
   c. describe what can be done with compost

3. Which of the following is **not** something the author mentions to support his proposal?
   a. Composting would teach students about science.
   b. It does not cost anything to make compost.
   c. Students could study temperature and moisture through composting.

Bye Bye Bike

Read the story below and then fill in the story map.

Emily hid her face as she neared the bike racks at school. "I hate my bike," she said to her best friend Julie, "It's so old and ugly!"

"I'll race you home," Julie said as she got on her bike. The girls pedaled down the sidewalk as fast as they could. Suddenly, Emily's pedals began to grind and squeak. Something was wrong with the chain. Emily slowly walked her bike back to her house to show her mom. She was almost glad it was broken—maybe it would be a chance to get a new bike. Emily's mom offered to have the bike fixed.

"Why bother?" Emily said angrily. "I don't care if I never ride it again."

The next day, Emily walked to school, but it took her a very long time, and she missed being with her friends. Emily got up earlier the next day, but she was still running late. Her dad drove her to school. She was embarrassed to drive up to school with her dad. This was even worse than riding her ugly bike!

After school that day, Emily went with her mom to the bike shop, and it was only a few dollars to get the repairs. Mom even let her pick a new paint color!

Characters: _____

Setting: _____

Plot: _____

Problem: _____

_____

Solution: _____

_____

_____

Theme: _____

_____

_____

Naps and Caps

Use **capital letters** for the following:

magazines and newspapers: *World News*
works of art: *Mona Lisa*
songs: "Spring Melody"
organizations: Girl Scouts
first word of a quote: My mother said,
"Please set the alarm clock."

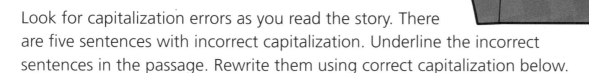

Look for capitalization errors as you read the story. There are five sentences with incorrect capitalization. Underline the incorrect sentences in the passage. Rewrite them using correct capitalization below.

I had a big night planned with my friends in the stargazers club. We had been reading about stargazing in the weather section of the newspaper. The *Fairmont city times* said that there would be a lot of falling stars that night. My dad agreed to take us on a campout, but he warned me, "You have to take a nap before we go!" I tried listening to classical music to fall asleep. I started to drift off, but then the song "flight of the bumblebees" came on and it woke me up. Perhaps reading my mom's issue of *growing garden* would put me to sleep. I couldn't find that magazine, but there was a book about artwork on the table. I flipped through the pages, and before I knew it I was snoozing. When I woke up, the book was open to the painting *starry night* by Van Gogh. Thanks to my afternoon nap I'd be able to stay up to see my own starry night!

1. _____

2. _____

3. _____

4. _____

5. _____

Shrink and Think

Contractions and **abbreviations** make words shorter.

For example:

I will	he would	should not	Street	January	Junior
⬇	⬇	⬇	⬇	⬇	⬇
I'll	he'd	shouldn't	St.	Jan.	Jr.

Read each word or pair of words. Circle the correct contraction or abbreviation.

1. he will	he'il	he'wl	he'll
2. Avenue	Aven.	Ave.	Av.
3. would not	wouldn't	wouldnt	would'nt
4. Doctor	Dr.	Doc.	Dt.
5. will not	willn't	wilon't	won't
6. September	SeP.	Sept.	Septm.
7. should have	should've	shouldha've	shouldv'e
8. Senior	sr.	Sr.	Se.
9. they are	theyr'e	theya're	they're
10. Saturday	Sat.	Satdy.	Sa.

Read All About It

Magazines and **newspapers** have lots of information. They are printed every day, week, or month. They are also organized differently than a book.

issue	article	headline	classified ads	section	table of contents

Solve each riddle. Write the correct word on the line. Use the words in the word bank.

1. A newspaper is divided into many of these parts. I could be about travel, business, or weather. _____

2. I am in magazines and newspapers. I am a short text or story about something. There are many of me in each newspaper or magazine. _____

3. I am a big title on the very front of a newspaper. I am the first thing the reader sees. I try to get people's attention! _____

4. Newspapers and magazines have me in the front. I show all the articles that are inside and what page each one begins on. _____

5. If you want to buy or sell something, you might look at me. I am a special section in the newspaper. _____

6. I help keep track of which season, month, or day a newspaper or magazine is printed. _____

Sorting out Stories

There are different types of imaginative stories. Read the clues below and figure out which type of story is being described. Use the clues to fill in the crossword puzzle with the correct word.

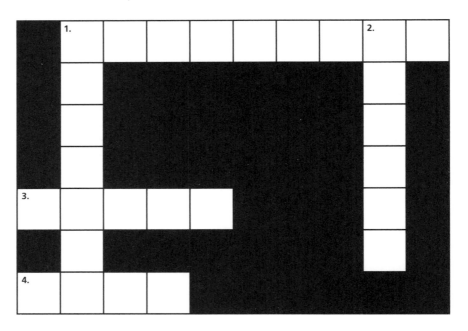

Down

1. Stories from this genre have something make-believe. There is usually something magical or impossible. These stories can take place during any time—past, present, or future.

2. This type of story is usually about a person or place. It is based on facts but is usually exaggerated or not completely true.

Across

1. Magical creatures, monsters, princesses, and princes are often characters in this kind of story.

3. These stories always have a moral or lesson at the end. The main characters are usually animals that can talk.

4. This is a story that tries to explain how the world works. These stories are set in a time long ago, before history began.

Speedy Spelling

Complete each sentence. Circle the correctly spelled word in parentheses.

1. All the drivers had _____ and it was almost time for the race.
(arrived / arrives / arived)

2. First they had to check all the _____ on the car and make sure everything
was set. (sistems / systims / systems)

3. All the race car drivers put on their _____. (unaforms / uniforms / uniforns)

4. The race started and the cars took off in a _____.
(whirlwind / wirlwind / wherlwind)

5. Nobody could _____ how fast they were going. (beleive / believe / beleve)

Read each sentence. Circle the misspelled word and fix it.

6. A chorous of fans cheered for the racers as they sped around the track.

7. One car that had been in the back was catching up and moving tword the front.

8. That car suprised everyone as it sped across the finish line in first place.

9. When the race had finished, the fans clapped and the driver celabrated.

10. He got the fastest time and would be famouse for winning the race.

Word Analogies

Word **analogies** are like puzzles. First you have to figure out why the two words go together. Then you can figure out which word completes the set.

For example:

> Ballet is to dance as soccer is to sports.
> The first word is specific and the second word is general.

> Flower is to petal as loaf is to slice.
> The first word names the whole item and the second word names a part.

Complete each analogy. Circle the correct word.

1. Shark is to ocean as alligator is to _____.
   a. crocodile
   b. swamp
   c. pond
   d. reptile

2. Scissors are to cutting as crayons are to _____.
   a. colors
   b. artwork
   c. painting
   d. coloring

3. Hunger is to thirst as shy is to _____.
   a. nervous
   b. excited
   c. outgoing
   d. happy

4. Gigantic is to huge as greedy is to _____.
   a. generous
   b. angry
   c. jealous
   d. selfish

5. Blanket is to soft as ice is to _____.
   a. cold
   b. water
   c. cube
   d. freezer

6. Thermometer is to temperature as scale is to _____.
   a. heavy
   b. balance
   c. weight
   d. length

Rainforest Research

Doing **research** on a subject means finding and gathering information. Different kinds of books can give different types of information. Nonfiction books and reference books like encyclopedias help us do research.

These students are writing reports about the rainforest. Read the description of what each student is researching. Then match the description to the book that would help that student find the right information. Write the letter on the line.

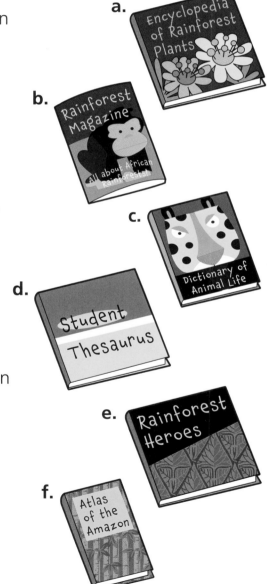

1. _____ Rachel is researching different plants found in the rainforest. She wants to find some general information about these plants.

2. _____ Ben is already writing his report about rainforests in Africa. Now he needs help finding synonyms for some of the words in his report.

3. _____ Helen is researching rainforests in Brazil. She wants to see a map of where the rainforests are located.

4. _____ Drew wants to write a biography about someone who has been important to the rainforests.

5. _____ Stacy is looking for information about African rainforests. She wants to read some articles that she can use for her report.

6. _____ Bret is reading an article about rainforest animals. Some of the words are unfamiliar. He wants to find out the meaning of these unknown words.

a. Encyclopedia of Rainforest Plants

b. Rainforest Magazine — All about African Rainforests

c. Dictionary of Animal Life

d. Student Thesaurus

e. Rainforest Heroes

f. Atlas of the Amazon

A Story from Scotland

Long ago in Scotland, there was a wise king named Robert the Bruce. His country was at war with England. Robert's army had been beaten in many battles, and he had to hide in a cave. It seemed impossible to win the war.

One rainy day, Robert the Bruce saw a spider having trouble spinning her web, but the spider never lost hope, and finally, attached her thread to the wall.

"If that spider can keep trying, I can try again as well," Robert said. He gathered his army together for another battle. This time, they won the battle! England's army was pushed back, and Scotland was free.

Read each question. Circle the correct answer.

1. This story would best be described as a _____.

   a. fable

   b. legend

   c. myth

2. At the beginning of the story, how does Robert the Bruce feel?

   a. He is hopeless and feels like a failure.

   b. He feels inspired to keep fighting.

   c. He is angry with his army for losing.

3. Watching the spider succeed helps Robert the Bruce feel _____.

   a. strength and courage

   b. tired and bored

   c. pride

4. What is the theme or lesson learned?

   a. Always look before you leap.

   b. In unity there is much strength.

   c. If at first you don't succeed, try again.

The Silkworm and the Spider

One day a silkworm was hard at work spinning silk for a princess. She spun very carefully and paid close attention to her job. Suddenly, a spider came along. Quickly and carelessly, she spun a giant web.

"I am a better worker than you are because I work so quickly," said the spider.

"I suppose," said the silkworm as she continued to spin, "but your webs are traps. People destroy them. Kings and queens treasure my silk. It is art and takes time."

Read each question. Circle the correct answer.

1. This story is best described as a _____.

  a. fable

  b. legend

  c. myth

2. What moral does the story teach?

  a. The fastest worker always does the best job.

  b. True art is made with care and patience.

  c. Art is pretty and delicate like a spider web.

Compare this story with the story on page 84. Check which story each description is about. If it describes both, check both columns.

	Robert the Bruce	Silkworm and Spider
3. A spider spins a web		
4. The spider does not put much care into her web.		
5. The spider helps another character realize something		
6. The animals in the story can talk to people and each other		
7. The story is about a real person but may not be completely true		

Submarine Summaries

A **summary** gives the most important ideas in a passage. A summary does not include all the details and supporting ideas. When you summarize, say things in your own words instead of repeating the passage.

Read each passage. Circle the best summary.

1. A submarine needs to be able to sink down and rise upward in the water. A sub has special tanks that hold air and water. When the tanks are filled with water, the sub becomes heavy and sinks down deep. To make the sub lighter, air is pumped into the tanks and water is released.

   a. Submarine tanks fill up with water and make the sub heavy so it will sink.
   b. Water is replaced with air inside the tank to make a submarine lighter.
   c. A submarine uses air and water in its tanks to help it sink or rise.

2. Susan's dad planned a big surprise for her last day in Hawaii—a submarine ride! The submarine took them about 100 feet below the surface of the ocean. She saw colorful fish and even some sea turtles. The sub also rode by sunken ships.

   a. The Hawaiian submarine ride took Susan 100 feet below the water.
   b. Susan and her dad saw fish, turtles, and sunken ships on a Hawaiian submarine ride.
   c. The submarine ride was on Susan's last day of vacation in Hawaii.

3. One of the earliest submarines was made in 1776 by an American named David Bushnell. It was called "The Turtle" because it looked like a sea turtle floating in the water. The Turtle was the first to pump air inside the sub. Plus, it was the first sub used in battle!

   a. David Bushnell made a submarine that looked like a sea turtle.
   b. America's first submarine had many special features.
   c. The Turtle was the first submarine ever made.

Summing Things Up

To write a summary, you need to figure out the main idea of a passage. As you read, look for the most important information and ideas. Underline the important parts so you can see them clearly. Use the box to write some notes about what seems most important from the passage. Then write a short summary of each passage.

The bald eagle has been a symbol of the United States for many years. The eagle was chosen to be part of the U.S. seal because it is a strong, powerful bird. A bald eagle flies so high up it can go almost anywhere. People see it as a symbol of freedom. The bald eagle is pictured on our dollar bills, coins, and even stamps.

notes:

Summary: _____

_____

Bald eagle nests are really built to last! Bald eagles use sticks, grass, and moss to build their nests high in the treetops. These amazing birds reuse the same nest year after year. As they add to the nest each year, it gets bigger. Scientists studied one eagle nest in Ohio that was used for 34 years. It had grown to be 10 feet wide. Of all the birds in the world, bald eagles build some of the biggest and strongest nests.

notes:

Summary: _____

_____

Pick a Pattern

Choosing a pattern helps you organize your thoughts and ideas. There are different patterns you can use when you write.

sequential order: presents ideas or steps in order

cause & effect: explains how something leads to another event

compare-contrast: points out how two things are alike and different

proposition & support: gives an idea or opinion and backs it up

question & answer: poses a question and explains the answer

Each student has a different assignment. Think about which writing pattern would work best for each student's topic. Choose a pattern from the box and write it on the line.

sequential order	cause & effect	compare-contrast
proposition & support		question & answer

1. Dora is on the student council. She needs to write a passage giving her idea for a school fundraiser. She will back up her opinion with details and facts.

   _____

2. Wyatt is working on a science report. He used special drops in the water of his fish tank. Then he tested the water to see how it was affected. _____

3. Max needs to write a passage about how to fix a flat tire on a bicycle. He will break it down into easy-to-follow steps. _____

4. Brianne's report is going to be about the similarities between the banjo and guitar. Her report will also point out how the two instruments are different.

   _____

5. Terry is doing research on coral reefs. She wants to answer the question, "What animals live in a coral reef?" _____

Getting Organized

Read each passage. Think about how it is organized. Choose the pattern from the box that best describes the organization of each passage. Write it on the line.

| sequential order | cause & effect | compare-contrast | proposition & support |

1. Making your own pizza is easy and fun. First, you need to get your pizza dough ready. Begin by putting some flour down so the dough won't stick. You can use your hands or a rolling pin to flatten the dough to one-quarter inch thick. Next, spread tomato sauce on top of the dough. Finally, sprinkle grated cheese on top. The last step is to put your pizza in the oven and let it bake! _____

2. Not all pizzas are created alike! Two common types of pizza are Neapolitan and Sicilian. Neapolitan pizza is named after the city of Naples in Italy. This type of pizza is round and has a thin crust. Sicilian pizza is named after an Italian island, Sicily. It has a thicker crust and is often made in a square shape. Even though they have some differences, both Neapolitan and Sicilian pizza share the same basic ingredients—dough, sauce, and cheese. _____

3. What do people like on top of their pizza? It depends on where they live! Although pizza started in Italy, it soon spread into many other places. Each country has different flavors and foods, so pizza toppings are different too. Since Japan is an island, people there eat a lot of seafood. So, a favorite topping on Japanese pizza is eel or squid! _____

4. People love having pizza delivered, but not everyone wants a whole pizza. Pizza places should start delivering slices of pizza. This way, people could order the exact amount and type of pizza they want. Small families wouldn't have to order more pizza than they can eat. Pizza would not be wasted or thrown away. A large family wouldn't have to agree on the toppings. Everyone could order a slice of exactly what they want! Overall, delivering pizza by the slice would be a great idea.

_____

A Second Look

Revising means taking second look at a piece of writing. You can correct mistakes and find ways to improve the sentences.

Getting to Know Grandma

(1) My grandmother is a fascinating woman! (2) Her name is Fran Bailey.

(3) Fran grew up in Colorado on a ranch. (4) As a girl, she rode horses and helped with the animals. (5) She was like a cowgirl! (6) When she met my grandfather, they decided to explore other places. (7) She always told my grandfather, "Variety is the spice of life"

(8) Now Fran is 73 years old, but she does more than most of the kids I know! (9) She even writes a column for the "Grove City Gazette." (10) Everyone who knows Fran say that she is still putting spice in her life!

Read each question. Circle the correct answer.

1. How could you use an appositive to best join sentences 1 and 2?

  a. My grandmother is a fascinating woman, and her name is Fran Bailey.

  b. Fran Bailey is my grandmother and also is a fascinating woman.

  c. My grandmother, Fran Bailey, is a fascinating woman.

2. Which is the correct way to punctuate sentence 7?

  a. She always told my grandfather, "Variety is the spice of life!"

  b. She always told my grandfather. 'Variety is the spice of life'.

  c. She always told my grandfather "Variety is the spice of life"

3. Which is the correct way to write the title in sentence 9?

  a. "Grove City" gazette

  b. *Grove City Gazette*

  c. correct as is

4. Which is the **best** way to write sentence 10?

  a. Everyone who knows Fran says that she is still putting spice in her life!

  b. Everyone who knows Fran said that she is still putting spice in her life!

  c. leave as is

Ready to Revise!

The passage below was written by a student. It has mistakes and there are sentences that can be improved.

(1) Charlottesville is a small city with a big personality. (2) Only about 40,000 people live in this quaint Virginia city. (3) People who live in Charlottesville are proud of its history. (4) Three U.S. presidents—Thomas Jefferson James Monroe and James Madison—are all from Charlottesville. (5) Thomas Jefferson's famous home is still in

Charlottesville. (6) The name of his home is "Monticello" and people can visit it.

(7) Charlottesville is a beautiful city year round. (8) The nearby Blue Ridge Mountains and Rivanna River. (9) The mountains are perfect for hiking in the summer and skiing in the winter. (10) It snow in the winter and rain in the spring. (11) The summers are not too hot. (12) So people get a little bit of everything!

(13) People from Charlottesville like to say "It's the best place to live in America. (14) Magazines like money, reader's digest, and many others have ranked Charlottesville as one of the top cities to live in. (15) It sounds like they might be right!

Follow the directions to revise the passage.

1. Combine sentences 5 and 6.

_____

2. Add commas to sentence 4 to make it correct.

_____

3. Revise sentence 8 to make it a complete sentence.

_____

4. Correct the verbs in sentence 10 and write it correctly.

_____

5. Rewrite sentence 13 using correct punctuation marks.

_____

6. Rewrite sentence 14 using correct capitalization.

_____

Answer Key

Page 4
1. call
2. funny
3. long a
4. shy
5. hour
6. long i
7. learn
8. scene

Page 5
1. c
2. a

Possible answers:
3. Maine produces a lot of blueberries that are shipped all over the world.

Page 6
1. d
2. Answers will vary.

Page 7
1. Try on the smallest jeans first. Imperative
2. What are you wearing to the party? Interrogative
3. Before you buy the shoes with the polka dots (incomplete)
4. I can't believe she spilled punch on her skirt! Exclamatory
5. Shopping for a new pair of winter boots (incomplete)
6. This T-shirt is comfortable. Declarative
7.–10. Answers will vary.

Page 8
1. e
2. a
3. b
4. c
5. d
6. ketch-up
7. wa-ter-mel-on
8. to-ma-to
9. a-vo-ca-do
10. mus-tard

Page 9
1. b
2. a
3. d
4. c

Page 10
1. The girls baked a cake and made a card.
2. They forgot about the cake in the oven.
3. They had time to set up a sundae bar.

Page 11
1. Deon and Nick were both on the blue team compound subject, simple predicate
2. The blue team hoped to win and practiced for a long time simple subject, compound predicate
3. The teacher blew her whistle and started the game simple subject, compound predicate
4. The red team and the blue team played their best compound subject, simple predicate
5. Everyone tried to score points to win the game simple subject, compound predicate
6. The teacher and her students came to the scoreboard compound subject, simple predicate
7. Deon and the rest of his team saw the scoreboard and cheered compound subject, compound predicate
8. The blue team scored the most points and won the game! simple subject, compound predicate

Page 12
1. e
2. c
3. b
4. f
5. d
6. a

Page 13
1. Rules & Hours
2. After-School Classes
3. Computer Lab
4. Rules & Hours
5. After-School Classes
6. Computer Lab
7. After-School Classes
8. Computer Lab

Page 14
1. b
2. c

Page 15
1. simple
2. simple
3. compound
4. simple
5. compound
6. simple
7. compound
8. simple

Page 16
A.
3
1
4
2

B.
3
4
2
1

C.
2
1
5
4
3

Page 17
Paragraphs will vary.

Page 18

Page 19
1. d
2. c

This paragraph will give reasons why kids should be able to ride their skateboards to school.

Page 20
The following sentences should be underlined in the passage:
First, I heard rain tapping on the roof like the sound of scampering mice.
The window felt as cold as ice.
Soon, the wind howled like screeching tires.
The wind was like a giant rake, pushing and dragging leaves across the ground.
Suddenly, it was as quiet as a library.
1.–5. Answers will vary.

Page 21
1. noun
2. article
3. adjective
4. pronoun
5. article
6. adjective
7. verb
8. pronoun
9. noun
10. verb

Page 22
1. preschool
2. unusual
3. impatient
4. misbehave
5. inappropriate
6. dishonest
7. replant
8. misspell
9. imperfect
10. recount
11. uncover
12. prewash
13. incomplete
14. disagree

Page 23
1. a
2. d

Page 24
1. c Dinnertime at our house is a race.
2. e Today's homework is a piece of cake.
3. d Uncle Jim is a giant!
4. f After lunch, the kitchen was a disaster.
5. b These kids are wild animals.
6. a This week was a roller coaster.
7. g In the morning, my brother is a bear.
8. h Music class is always a party.

Page 25
1. travels
2. spent
3. carries
4. leave
5. found
6. built
7. slept
8. hold

Page 26
1. explorer
2. darkness
3. noticeable
4. wooden
5. colorful
6. proudly
7. inspection
8. worthless
9. peaceful ness
10. careful ly
11. comfortab ly
12. direction less

Page 27
1. You should water the lawn in the early morning or the evening when it's cool.
2. The class has a substitute teacher for the day.

Page 28
1. c
2. b

Page 29
1. "Tiger Finds a Teacher"
2. "The Ungrateful Tiger"
3. both
4. "Tiger Finds a Teacher"
5. both
6. both

Page 30
1. Paragraph 1
2. The topic is what the writer would do on a perfect Saturday.
3. Paragraph 2 is about what the writer would do in the morning.
4. Paragraphs 2, 3, and 4
5. Paragraph 5

Page 31
Answers will vary.

Page 32
1. technique
2. average
3. diced
4. stir
5. slender
6. smell
7. cautious
8. feast

Page 33
1. c
2. c
3. a
4. c

Page 34
1. breeze whispered
2. angry waves
3. cruel raindrops
4. cookies called out
5. photos that told stories
6. tired shoes
7.–10. Answers will vary.

Page 35
1. lightly; how
2. soon; when
3. quickly; how
4. often; when
5. carefully; how
6. loudly; how
7. today; when
8. early; when
9. down; where
10. outside; where

Page 36

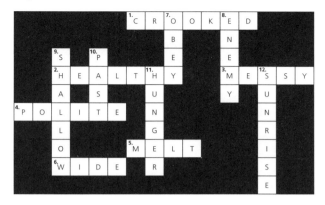

Page 37
3 A chocolate bar in Spencer's pocket melted.
4 Spencer put some popcorn kernels by the radar machine and they popped.
8 Small microwave ovens were sold for people to use.
1 It was after World War II, and Percy Spencer went into a science lab.
2 Spencer walked by a radar machine that used microwaves.
5 A raw egg was placed near the machine.
6 A scientist stepped close to the egg and it exploded in his face.
7 A 750-pound, five-and-a-half foot microwave oven was created.

Page 38
1. We were given a list that was a mile long!
2. In no time at all, I had found the first few things.
3. Pretty soon my bag was full and weighed a ton!
4. I was being cooked alive!
5. At the end of the day, my feet were killing me.

Page 39
1. This year, the big party was held at the park. *(circle at)*
2. Some kids put their presents in pretty gift bags. (circle *in*)
3. The weather was sunny and warm during the party. (circle *during*)
4. All the kids sang "Happy Birthday" to the birthday girl. (circle *to*)
5. We put the cake on a picnic table and cut pieces. (circle *on*)
6. The birthday girl got the biggest slice of cake! (circle *of*)
7. Kids enjoyed eating cake before the presents were opened. (circle *before*)
8. Everyone went home with a fun party favor. (circle *with*)
9.–12. Answers will vary.

Page 40
Possible answers:
1. sore, painful
2. gentle
3. kind, loving, compassionate
4. reach, spread, lengthen, extend
5. drag out, prolong
6. length

Page 41
1. c
2. a
3. Possible answer: How did people make popcorn long ago?
4. Possible answer: What kinds of popcorn toppings are there?

Page 42
1. The autumn leaves were as red as apples. simile
2. It had been raining for an eternity. hyperbole
3. A gentle breeze kissed my face. personification
4. Perfect pears were picked for the pie. alliteration
5. The wind swooshed through the trees. onomatopoeia
6. I was dying to have some of the hot chocolate. hyperbole
7. The pumpkins were bowling balls in my arms. metaphor
8. Storm clouds covered the sun like a blanket. simile
9. The flowers complained about the change of weather. personification
10. My wool sweater was my best friend. metaphor
11. Curtis the cat curled up on the cozy couch. alliteration
12. Bright flames crickled and crackled in the fireplace. onomatopoeia

Page 43
1. and
2. so
3. or
4. and; or
5. so
6. or; so
7. but
8. so
9. or
10. and

Page 44
Examples of sensory details
Sight
frosted in every imaginable color
fancy letters on the window
Smell
clothes smelled like fertilizer
sweet smell surrounded me
Sound
stomach growled so loud
collapsed on the couch with a thud
Touch
hands were raw and blistered
it felt light and delicate
Taste
moist and delicious
sugary sprinkles melted

Page 45
Narratives will vary.

Page 46
1. a
2. d
3. c
4. b
5. c
6. a
7. d
8. a

Page 47
1. skywriting
2. both
3. sky typing
4. both
5. skywriting
6. skywriting
7. sky typing
8. both

Page 48
1. c   3. c
2. a   4. b

Page 49
1. My family likes to go skiing in Aspen, Colorado.
2. Before playing in snow you should put on gloves, boots, and a scarf.
3. Rock Canyon, the park right by my house, is a great place to go sledding.
4. You need patience, determination, and warm mittens to build a good snowman.
5. The biggest snowball fight happened on Saturday, March 3.
6. Everything is on sale at the Snow Hut, the best place to get skis, sleds, and skates.
7. December, January, and February usually get a lot of snowfall.
8. A dazzling performer on the ice, the skater delighted the crowd.

Page 50
aud: auditorium, audible
form: reform, format
man: manual, manage
pict: depict, picture
brev: abbreviation, brief
scrib: script, describe
phon: telephone, phonics
flex: flexible, reflex

Page 51

	solar salt	evaporated salt	rock salt
1. Where is it found?	ocean water	beneath the earth	mines
2. How is it made?	sun and wind dry up pools of water	water is pumped through tunnels then removed by vacuum	explosives shake big rocks loose
3. What is it used for?	softening water	baking	melting ice

Page 52
1. creepy
2. hopeful
3. lonely
4. angry
5. carefree
6. exciting

Page 53
Answers may vary.
1. Jason finds a plank of wood, but it is too long for the go-cart.
2. Marvin, who has experience using tools, helps cut the wood.
3. Jason and Marvin sand the wood and paint it black.
4. They attach the wheels from an old baby stroller.
5. Now it's time to attach a soft, comfortable seat.
6. Foster Park, the best place for go-carts, is where Jason takes his first ride.

Page 54
1. trans/port: to carry over or across
2. inter/lace: to weave something in between
3. uni/form: one form or shape
4. bio/logy: the study of life
5. auto/mobile: a car or other vehicle that moves by itself
6. inter/national: between nations
7. bio/graphy: story of someone's life
8. micro/scope: a tool for seeing small things
9. multi/purpose: having more than one purpose or use
10. semi/circle: a half circle
11. multi/part: many parts
12. semi/sweet: partly or halfway sweet

Page 55
1. fact
2. fact
3. opinion
4. fact
5. opinion
6. fact
7. opinion
8. opinion
9.–12. Answers will vary.

Page 56
Answers may vary.
1. Frog wanted one short day and one short night.
2. Bear wanted six months of day and six months of night.
3. Frog was friendly and listened to the animals. Bear was a bully.
4. The animals decided to go with Frog's plan and have one short day and one short night.

Page 57
Possible answers:
1. Some animals wanted daylight all the time and others wanted night all the time.
2. Squirrel pointed out that Raccoon has both light and dark rings on his tail in equal parts.
3. They decided to divide up day and night into equal parts and repeat the pattern.
4. Bear scratched Squirrel's back with his claws.
5. a
6. c

Page 58
1. b
2. c
3. c

Page 59
Reports will vary.

Page 60
1. c
2. c
3. a
4. a

Page 61
1. cause
    effect
2. effect

cause
3. effect
cause

Page 62
1. The king thought that only a boy could be the next ruler.
2. Altyn-Aryg used the sword her father gave her to kill the Snake Prince.
3. When the King heard she had killed the Snake Prince and let everyone free, he knew she could be the next ruler.
4. This is a fairy tale because it has a monster and is about a princess.

Page 63
1. "The puppy ran out the front door!" my sister yelled.
2. As I ran out the door I yelled back, "We have to catch him quickly."
3. "He's getting away," Denise said in a panicked voice.
4. "I have an idea," I said. "Let's split up and try to corner him."
5. Denise agreed and said, "I'll go to the right and you go to the left."
6. "Look," I said, "the puppy is in Mrs. Howard's garden."
7. "I hope he doesn't trample on her flowers," Denise said.
8. "We've almost got him," I said as we crept closer.
9. "Gotcha!" Denise yelled as she scooped the puppy up into her arms.
10. We both hugged the puppy and I said, "I knew we could catch him."

Page 64
1. b
2. a
3. c
4. a
5. c
6. b

Page 65
1. inform
2. persuade
3. persuade
4. inform
5. entertain
6. entertain

Page 66
1. a
2. b

Page 67
1. his or Brad's
2. yours
3. theirs
4. her or Angela's
5. mine
6. ours
7. his or Paul's
8. his

Page 68
1. All the kids <u>know</u> that there is <u>no</u> food allowed in the living room.
2. Always wear a <u>pair</u> of gloves before going to the <u>pear</u> tree to pick fruit.
3. The bruise on your <u>heel</u> will take about three weeks to <u>heal</u>.
4. I would <u>accept</u> your invitation to play, <u>except</u> I have piano practice.
5. If you pay a small <u>fare</u> the bus will take you to the front entrance of the <u>fair</u>.
6. Everyone <u>stares</u> at my sister when she comes down the <u>stairs</u> with a crazy hairdo.
7. As the mechanic fixed the <u>brake</u> pedal, I waited in the <u>break</u> room.
8. Over the weekend I will <u>be</u> as busy as a <u>bee</u>!
9. too
10. which
11. there
12. you're

Page 69
1. correct
2. correct
3. There are six kids on the waiting list to check out the book <u>Palm Tree Paradise</u>.
4. I found an old copy of <u>Little Red Riding Hood</u> at a used bookstore
5. This month I read about how to recycle in a magazine called <u>Green Kids</u>.
6. correct
7. I always check in the classified ads in the <u>Crescent City Chronicle</u>.
8. correct

Page 70
1. b
2. a
3. c
4. a

Page 71
1. Both
2. Interview
3. Passage
4. Interview
5. Both

Page 72
1. b
2. b
3. a

Page 73
Reports will vary.

Page 74
1. courtyard
2. headache
3. sidewalk
4. headline
5. ponytail
6. gumballs

Possible answers include:
water: underwater, waterproof, watermelon
sand: sandstorm, sandcastle, sandbox, sandpaper
butter: buttermilk, butterscotch, butterfly, buttercup
sun: sunshine, sunbeam, sunburn, sunflower

Page 75
1. c
2. a
3. b

Page 76
Possible answers:
Characters: Emily, her best friend Julie, and her mother
Setting: Emily's house and school
Plot: Emily is sick of her old ugly bike. Then it breaks down and she realizes how much she needs it.
Problem: Emily's bike is broken, but she thinks it's so ugly she doesn't want to get it fixed. She has to find another way to get to school.
Solution: Emily decides to have her bike fixed and she paints it a new color.
Theme: Sometimes we don't realize how much we need something until it's gone.

Page 77
1. I had a big night planned with my friends in the Stargazers Club.
2. The *Fairmont City Times* said that there would be a lot of falling stars that night.
3. I started to drift off, but the song "Flight of the Bumble-bees" came on and it woke me up.
4. Perhaps reading my mom's is-sue of *Growing Garden* would put me to sleep.
5. When I woke up, the book was open to the painting *Starry Night* by Van Gogh.

Page 78
1. he'll
2. Ave.
3. wouldn't
4. Dr.
5. won't
6. Sept.
7. should've
8. Sr.
9. they're

10. Sat.

Page 79
1. section
2. article
3. headline
4. table of contents
5. classified ads
6. issue

Page 80
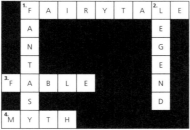

Page 81
1. arrived
2. systems
3. uniforms
4. whirlwind
5. believe
6. (chorous); chorus
7. (tword); toward
8. (suprised); surprised
9. (celabrated); celebrated
10. (famouse);famous

Page 82
1. b
2. d
3. c
4. d
5. a
6. c

Page 83
1. a
2. d
3. f
4. e
5. b
6. c

Page 84
1. b
2. a
3. a
4. c

Page 85
1. a
2. b
3. both
4. Silkworm and Spider
5. both
6. Silkworm and Spider
7. Robert the Bruce

Page 86
1. c
2. b
3. c

Page 87
Summaries will vary.

Page 88
1. proposition & support
2. cause & effect
3. sequential order
4. compare & contrast
5. question & answer

Page 89
1. sequential order
2. compare & contrast
3. cause & effect
4. proposition & support

Page 90
1. c
2. a
3. b
4. a

Page 91
Possible answers:
1. Thomas Jefferson's famous home, "Monticello," is still in Charlottesville, and people can visit it.
2. Three U.S. presidents—Thomas Jefferson, James Monroe, and James Madison—are all from Charlottesville.
3. The Blue Ridge Mountains and Rivanna River are nearby.
4. It snows in the winter and rains in the spring.
5. People from Charlottesville like to say, "It's the best place to live in America."
6. Magazines like *Money*, *Read-er's Digest*, and many others have ranked Charlottesville as one of the top cities to live in.